Good Morning, Sunrise

Good Morning, Sunrise

Triumphing over cancer is possible

Georges Córdoba

QualeVita
**Living Well,
Learning and Sharing**

Good Morning, Sunrise. Triumphing over cancer is possible
© Georges Córdoba, 2019 ✉ coach.georges@qualevita.com

ISBN: 978-980-18-0084-2

Correction: Damarys Castro

Cover photo: *Sunrise in front of the sea* (detail).
Venezuelan coast, 2009; ✉ sainzphotos@gmail.com
© Archive from La Agencia de la Palabra for this edition

Authors portrait: Francisco González
http://www.zalezphoto.com ✆ 01305 4670204

Concept, design, layout
and editorial coordination:
  Alfredo Sainz

La Agencia de la Palabra
✆ 058212 3157426
  Caracas, 2019

In One Word

I n this world, God sends us special people who cross our paths and touch our souls. They are known as angels. One of these angels is Georges Córdoba. I remember the day I met him. My husband, Mario, and Georges were childhood friends. At once, they reconnected and rekindled a beautiful friendship. I was sitting on the sofa when Georges approached me, and we began talking. Instantly, it felt like a heart to heart connection.

During that time, I was writing the book, *Transform Your Loss. Your Guide to Strength and Hope.* When I met Georges and learned about his incredible story of transformation, I asked him to write the prologue for my book. He wrote it and it meant a lot to me. The impact that Georges' prologue had on people when being read at the book reads resonated with me.

People would call me to ask about Georges; they knew he was a special human being. Georges is special indeed. For a long time, we spoke about the message Georges had for the world, and how writing a book can help spread it.

With love and willingness, it was time for him to share his life experiences, the lessons he learned and seeds of love with the world. Now, my turn has come to write a prologue with all my love for this special book. has come, and I write this prologue, for this very special book. I suggest, dear reader, that as you read, do so with an open heart to receive the messages of transformation and welcome them into your heart. In the same way that a seed grows and develops when planted in fertile soil, allow this message full of love, hope, and spiritual strength to develop and grow within your own soul.

As a therapist and life coach, I understand how important using inner capabilities is when people are trying to transform their lives. However, sometimes, blinded by pain or fear, we forget that we have this inner power. The constant questions we ask ourselves when we are diagnosed with cancer, or when we face a difficult life transition, can weaken us not only physically, but also spiritually. In this book, Georges tells us how he responded to those questions that filled his mind and how he used different strategies, internal and external, to face hardship and transform his life. He wanted to set an example of faith, positivity, and love to others. This book is a spiritual, emotional, and even physical guide for those who are suffering from cancer, for their families. and even for those who do not suffer from cancer. The principles shared here can be used as guidelines to live a life with greater meaning, to live more from the inside out. We live in a fast-paced world with many distractions that can distract us from being true to who we really are.

In addition, Georges reminds us the importance of reconnecting with who we are, with that essence that makes us special. Georges' essence was precisely what had such a profound affect when I met him. In this book, he opens his heart to readers with the intention of sharing valuable tools that can be used in times of doubt, pain, despair, or defeat. You have the will power within you, and Georges encourages to use it to achieve a definitive change in life. This though reminds me of a saying my father used to say, "We should learn the greatest of the arts: knowing how to live".

Georges shares with us how he has mastered this art and reveals that cancer was the catalyst, the flame that provoked this change in him, this need to help, these desires to make a difference, to influence others, and to be a leader in the battle against cancer. Everything begins with us. The quality of life depends on a person's attitude, conviction, and desire to live. The mountain that Georges had to climb was very rough and demanding, with falls. However, his attitude, faith, and positive thinking has helped him reach the top and overcome, as he calls it, his opponent cancer. Georges did not go into denial. He confronted his reality, face to face and took possession of all the tools that were within his reach, and those tools that he did not have, he sought out.

The beauty of Georges is that he does not deny the emotions he experienced. He acknowledged and validated each one of them. That is the only way to confront and overcome challenging events. The important thing is not to ignore emotions, but to recognize them, understand them, and decide what to do about them. From the use of metaphors to visualizations, Georges leads us with much love and faith toward the path of hope, self-care, and acceptance

In this book Georges reminds us of our human potential for our own lives and the lives of others. Let us listen to his suggestions that made a difference in his life. They may also make a difference in yours. In the end, everything is summed up in a single word: love. This book is filled with it: love of oneself, love of one's neighbor, love towards God.

Thank you, Georges, my soul friend, for this gift. Thank you for your life, and may God bless you.

LIGIA HOUBEN

The Song I was Born to Sing

This book is dedicated to everyone that has been
touched by cancer: patients and survivors.
To their relatives and their caregivers:
for being angels along the way.

To Nuni, and to all of my angels:
you are all gifts from God,
brought together to teach me the healing
powers of love and service.
I thank God for giving me a second chance
to sing the song that I was born to sing

Spring has passed. Summer has gone.
Winter is here... and the song that I meant to sing
remains unsung. For I have spent my days
stringing and unstringing my instrument.
RABINDRANATH TAGORE

Introduction

This book is written for everyone who has heard a cancer diagnosis and is dealing with it right now. Mine was "malignant melanoma later progressing to metastasis in the brain." At first, I just couldn't understand it. What? What are you saying? I feel perfectly fine! No, no it cannot be! This cannot be happening! What do you mean I have cancer?

Dear reader, I hope that by reading this book you will find strength and hope as you walk through your process. I hope you will understand that the stress, worry, and fear you are experiencing right now are normal.

Sometimes you may wonder if anyone understands what you are going through, and the answer is yes! We, survivors, understand exactly what you are thinking and feeling right now. I know what you are going through because they were the same thoughts I had.

Here are some facts you may not know: according to the National Cancer Institute, "in the US, the number of people living beyond a cancer diagnosis reached nearly 14.5 million in 2014 and is expected to rise to almost 19 million by 2024". These statistics are only for the United States! Imagine the figures worldwide!

These encouraging statistics, I believe, are possible because we are beginning to combine conventional forms of treatment with holistic alternatives to confront the disease.

Now allow me to tell you a little bit about myself and how I earned my "Cancer Survivor" title.

On Sunday afternoon, in August 2002, three weeks after my dear mother lost her battle with lung cancer, I was home siting on our pool deck while the kids were playing pool volleyball. I was forty-two years old at the time. I am and have always been an outdoor type of person. My parents told me I learned how to swim before I walked. I have spent most of my life under the sun, swimming and snorkeling the beautiful Atlantic and Caribbean waters of Venezuela. I've played tennis since the age of five and competitively at New Mexico State University. I also surfed every time I had a chance. I loved to be outside: sun, sun, and more sun.

That August day, as I was sunbathing by the pool, I began to repeatedly scratch the top of my head, to the point that I started bleeding. I thought it was probably a pimple. But I still asked my wife, Naomi, to check it out. She looked at my bleeding spot and told me she did not like it. What do you mean? I asked. She didn't like it at all, and wanted to get it checked with a dermatologist. The next day, early Monday morning, she contacted our dermatologist to make an appointment. One of the office assistants said that the earliest the doctor could see me was a month down the road. My wife explained that my sore didn't look good at all and that she would greatly appreciate a call back if someone happened to cancel their appointment.

Later that afternoon Naomi received a call from the assistant stating that there was a cancelation for the next day, Tuesday at 9:00 a.m., so she booked the appointment. We got there at least half an hour early. As the doctor checked my sore, she asked me if I would mind allowing her visiting medical students to come in to the room to show them my sore. I nervously consented. She went ahead and showed my sore to the students and began to talk about its shape and the fact that it looked ulcerated. At that point, I started to get nervous. She scraped a sample for a biopsy and told me she would get back with me as soon as she got the results.

The following morning, my office assistant told me the doctor was on the line and wanted to talk to me immediately. A rush of adrenaline spread through my body as I picked up the phone. She told me that my biopsy came back positive for malignant melanoma and I urgently needed to see one of the two doctors she recommended on a report she was faxing me.

The events that took place after this for Naomi, our five young children, and I can only be compared to a tsunami. My cancer diagnosis suddenly appeared and nearly destroyed everything in its path, leaving a long road to recovery for all of us. Especially since Melanoma is a very aggressive form of skin cancer!

The first doctor recommended on the pathology report, Doctor Moffat, was on vacation and his schedule was booked. He would not be able to see me until the last week of September. Immediately I called Stefano one of my best friends, who is also a doctor and read the biopsy results to him. He asked me to fax the report to him, which I did. As soon as he received the results, he called to explain that time is of the essence. As he read the report, he stated that the doctors that were referred were the best in South Florida said the two doctors listed on the report were two of the best in South Florida, and they were very good friends. The fact that he knew of these doctors somehow gave me a sense of relief.

Stefano said the other doctor listed on the report, Dr. Weiss, was extremely talented. He told me that Dr. Weiss usually had a long waiting list. but being his former fellow student and good friend, he would see me immediately. Dr. Weiss opened a spot for me to go in to see him that afternoon. Amazingly, three days after we saw the sore, I was sitting at Dr. Weiss' ambulatory room undergoing a surgical procedure on top of my head to remove the ulcerated melanoma tumor. I am still very thankful for how quickly these initial steps happened.

After the procedure, Dr. Weiss strongly recommended an appointment with Dr. Moffat and suggested a lymph node sentinel biopsy as a reference to where the melanoma may have spread. I scheduled an appointment with Dr. Moffat as I waited to be released by Dr. Weiss. It seemed everything worked out smoothly. In retrospect, this sequence of events was when I realized the universe began to work in my favor.

As I anxiously waited to visit Dr. Moffatt, it was as though my body was going through a constant adrenaline rush. I felt overwhelmed, stressed, anxiety, disbelief, and I was full of questions. Between the phone ringing off the hook, telling and repeating the devastating news to our family, friends, and colleges, I couldn't help but to wonder how my five kids were going react to the news. They had just lost their grandmother to lung cancer three weeks ago and now, their dad has cancer. The thought of this made me feel restless and full of panic. As a young family, we had yet to experience our life together, and still our lives were about to fall apart. My marriage, my children, my family, my career, my goals—all of it was on the brink of collapsing. I couldn't believe it, this cannot be happening. I was in denial.

Naturally, I was going through a thought process. I was struggling with denial, the shock of it all, and the "Why me's?". Eventually, I came to accept the fact that I had cancer. I would tell myself, "Georges, man this is real. You are sick. You have an aggressive, unpredictable form of cancer. What are you going to do?"

I started to research malignant melanoma, and my findings were not encouraging. To date, the best chance to deal with this form of cancer was surgically because there is still no formal treatment for its cure. I must say that in the past few years there has been considerable progress toward more effective treatments to complement surgery, particularly in immune therapy.

I am blessed to have five, beautiful children, ages seven through fifteen, but now I am being told that I may not have the chance to see my children grow up! I was told that people with my diagnosis have about thirty-six months to live. I kept saying to myself, "What do I do now? How am I going to fight this? This can't be happening to me. This simply can't be!" But it was happening.

Two years after my diagnoses, I went into remission. However, almost five years later the disease came back and metastasized to my brain, and I was given a prognosis of six months to live. My life changed.

Knowing that the probabilities of surviving were very low and realizing that I was mortal, and death was knocking on my door, definitely impacted me. Thankfully, I survived this advanced-stage cancer, this tsunami almost took my family and I off the map. In the end, I won the battle, and this experience made us a stronger family.

Overall, my battle lasted ten years which included ten surgeries: two lymphadenectomies, three craniotomies, two Gamma Knife procedures, several biopsies, interferon alfa 2a, chemotherapy and radiotherapy, and GM-CSF, an immunologic treatment experiment.

To know the road ahead,
ask those coming back.
CHINESE PROVERB

The The purpose of this book is to describe the process I went through to regain my health, continue living a better, healthier life, and share the blessings I received while I battled this disease.

One morning, just before sunrise, my oldest son, Alejandro, and I rode to South Miami Beach. I remember that serene feeling, the silence of dawn. I began writing in my journal and Alejandro asked me if I was planning to write a book about my cancer. After some thought, I responded with, "Maybe, someday." He replied with, "If you do write a book, I suggest the title be 'Good Morning, Sunrise', because Paps, it looks like you have become friends with the sun, coming to the beach."

Finally, I had decided to write the book, and I took his suggestion for the title.

When I watch the sunrise or the sunset, it brings me peace. I constantly think about the miracle of life given to us.

Ironically, the sun, my mystical friend, nearly took my life. Today, I continue to be an outdoor person but with a greater sense of respect, prudently avoiding exposure to the sun at peak times of the day, when the ultraviolet radiation is highest.

When I admire
the wonders of a sunset
or the beauty of the moon,
my soul expands
in the worship of the creator.

MAHATMA GANDHI

The News

> After you are diagnosed with cancer, you may feel shock, disbelief, fear, anxiety, guilt, sadness, grief, depression, anger, and more. Each person may have some or all of these feelings, and each will handle them in a different way.
>
> THE AMERICAN CANCER SOCIETY

I lost my maternal grandfather to cancer when I was four years old, and I still remember the tragedy his death was to my family. Every time we heard that a family member or a friend had been diagnosed with cancer, our mind set was that of a death sentence. Another loved one was going to die because of cancer. I basically grew up believing that everyone diagnosed with cancer was indeed heading to the cemetery, and I feared this disease could come for me some day. I saw cancer as this unbeatable monster, and as the years passed this belief further rooted in me as relatives, friends, and unfortunately my mother fell victim to the disease.

No one is ever ready to hear that they have cancer.
It's normal for people with cancer to wonder why it happened
to them or to think life has treated them unfairly.

You may not even believe the diagnosis,
especially if you don't feel sick.
THE AMERICAN CANCER SOCIETY

My friends, I survived a very aggressive form of cancer, and am here to tell you that this disease is beatable. With new medical advances and a positive attitude, meditation, nutrition, and faith, cancer can be struck out of your life.

Remember,
you are no sicker the day of your diagnosis
than you were the day before.
VICKIE GIRARD
(author of *There's No Place Like Hope*)

Physically, I felt no different the day before nor the day I found out I had cancer. After the diagnosis, I knew that I was sick, my body was infested with this sickness. Now, this is where the mind becomes crucial, it can become your best or friend or your worst enemy. Attitude and knowledge become key allies; the more positive your attitude is, and the more knowledgeable you become to cancer, the better. Becoming knowledgeable of the disease and the steps you can do physically, emotionally, mentally, and spiritually to effectively fight it are important. The saying, "Knowledge is power" cannot ring truer than during this time!

If you allow everyone you know tell you that they know someone who took this or that potion, and suddenly the person was cured, can be extremely confusing and stressful. Surrounding yourself with positive energy can help you from people with pessimistic and fear-based attitudes toward cancer, because they can very easily pass their negative energy and fears of the disease to you. This person may be a friend, a relative, a colleague at work, a fellow patient, or even a stranger. You don't want to be around this type of negative energy; avoid it as much as possible.

Next are the probabilities and statistics based on research. Try not to get caught up on the statistics based on patient studies and group results. The point is that you are an individual, not a statistic. If, for instance, the probability of surviving a type of cancer with a particular diagnosis is 35%, that means thirty-five people out of one hundred survive.

If you allow yourself to be influenced by others, you will probably have to fight a much tougher battle. Study cancer as much as you can. You will find plenty of information online. In my case, I read about the different types of cancer and therapies, specifically malignant melanoma, and searched for complementing natural ways to help me fight it. I looked for all types of treatments used at the time, survival statistics, and more. I needed to understand, firsthand, what I was up against. I rarely looked for statistics, but when I did, I dared to defy the odds and be in the survivors' percent. The statistics became my personal barometer.

This can also be overwhelming: too much information to assimilate, but I believe it is essential to prepare and equip yourself with knowledge of, what I call "the opponent", to fight it. During the phase, I could not stop thinking, "It is me we are talking about here, not a friend or a friend of a friend or John or Mary's parents or my uncle or my aunt or someone down the street. This time we are talking about me."

When it comes to your relationship with the doctor, remember you are the boss, not the other way around. That's right, your doctors are your employees. You decided to hire them based on their professional record or because they were recommended to you. Make no mistake about it, you are paying your doctors to help you heal. You have the right to be demanding when it comes to receiving your results in a timely matter and to expect honest interpretation of them. I also recommend a second opinion, because it is your health and life you are dealing with.

Another important point to be clear about, is that you are the owner of your disease, and no one will care as much about your healing as you do. Life goes on, and everyone related to you has their own things to do as they live their daily routines. That goes for your doctors as well. There is no way they can be on top of your situation while they are simultaneously, taking care of their other patients. They can't possibly focus on just you. Stay in touch with your doctors so that they keep you on their minds. Call them and leave messages with their secretaries or call their nurses and leave them voicemails as well. These are good ways to keep you in their minds. Remember, you own your disease; no one will care as much about it and you hired your doctors to help you heal.

Thank God for traditional medicine and its advances. However, understanding that medicine is a trial and error process is important. Nothing is wrong about that. Experimentation is a fact we must accept, to open up to complementary alternative ways to help with the healing process.

During the time, I was confronting the many demands of this disease. I began to think about my mortality. I looked closer at my beliefs and values and what were the most important things in my life. Thinking about my diagnosis was hard and unpleasant, but once I accepted my reality, I began the journey of the rest of my life. Sadly, most of us need to be struck by a shocking impactful experience to realize what really matters.

To live is the rarest thing in the world.
Most people exist, that is all.
OSCAR WILDE

Life goes on, time keeps moving forward, people are caught up in their routines, no one has time to realize that the adversities we hear about happening to others, may one day happen to us. Life is fragile, and time goes by really fast, yet we live day by day as if we are going to live forever.

Why Me?

s I gripped the phone, the doctor said, "Try to stay calm, but you need to act quickly." I remember taking a deep breath and starting to speak to her with difficulty: "Doctor, are you saying I have cancer?". "Yes Mr. Cordoba. I am sorry, but I restate that you must contact one of the doctors as soon as possible."

After the call, I stayed in my chair, confused, remembering the tone of the doctor's voice and sense of urgency. Am I dreaming? What have I just heard? Do I have cancer? I could not believe it, or perhaps I didn't want to believe it. My adrenaline was maxed out, and I began to feel anxious and helpless. I was in shock. I could not believe it. Only those who have experienced receiving a cancer diagnosis can understand this state of mind, like an out of body experience.

"This can't be happening, could it be that there was a mistake in the results?", or so I thought. I was totally astonished, but I didn't want to think. I wanted to erase what I had just heard and simply continue with what I was doing before the call, but I could not. My mind kept trying to analyze what it just heard, while my emotions were all over the place responding to this bombshell news.

How can this be? Malignant melanoma? Why? Because of sun exposure? Or perhaps I was destined to have cancer because of my family history. I don't understand! I am an active athlete, and I eat healthy foods, I don't drink much, and I don't smoke. I am an honest person, and I am always willing to help others. I'm a family man, lovingly dedicated to my children. Why me? Days after my mother's passing, now me?! I don't understand. Wake up, Georges, this is a dream! THIS CAB NOT BE HAPPENING!

Once I received the doctor's fax with the results, I read them, still in shock and paralyzed. Malignant melanoma with ulcerated leisure. It was not a dream. I had cancer, it is true. I have the report with my name on it. Once again, the adrenaline all over the place and my mind going a million miles an hour. I have to call Naomi. What will I say to my kids? I kept trying to process what was happening to me. What do I do? Where do I start? How am I going to manage my work? How am I going to tell my father who is still processing mom's loss? I have not had the chance to process my mother's loss. Could it be that I will die before my children grow up? Will I be able to provide for my family? Will I leave my kids without a father? Questions, questions, and more questions without answers. I do not accept this, this can't be happening. They were very intense moments of denial, anxiety, anger, and fear. My God, what am I going to do?

In general, humans are afraid of dying. Many of us console ourselves in the faith that there is something better, for example, heaven and eternal life, beyond our physical lives. Everyone wants to go to heaven, but not today. That's right, our egos make us feel anxious and fearful. It is easy to say, "How sad, I heard that so and so has cancer, he had a heart attack, or she was diagnosed with chronic liver disease," but, when a tragedy happens to us, everything changes. An alarm is activated and reminds us that we are mortal, and this reality scares us, even if we are amongst those who believe that something better exists after this life.

I tried to fill up with courage to not break down, and finally I called Naomi. I am sure she suspected the results, but hearing the news impacted her greatly, and she broke down to tears, which caused me to cry and unload the anxiety and emotions that had accumulated since the doctor's call that morning. "What are we going to do with the kids? What are we going to tell the kids?", she asked me. I told her I was not sure, but I assured her that I would think of something during the rest of the afternoon. I told her I talked with Stefano who got me a late afternoon appointment that same day with the second doctor that appeared on the report. Still dazed by the news, she asked me if I wanted her to drive up and take me to the doctor, but because of the distance from each other's offices, I told her that my business partner would take me.

What we did not know was that the doctor would opt to extract the tumor right there in the office an ambulatory procedure. This explains Dr. Trowers' sense of urgency when she gave me the diagnosis.

Being seen and treated the same day of my diagnosis gave me a sense of calmness because I felt that I was acting as fast as Dr. Trowers suggested. Now, it was time to get home with my head bandaged and give the news to my children. Once again, the adrenaline and anxiety took over. I did not know if I could show tranquility and strength. Just a few weeks ago they had lost their grandmother to cancer. How would they react? Especially Claudia, our youngest, who at the time was seven years old. I had to talk to them. I have never been one for hiding things. I created a mental script so that I would appear strong as I talked to them, but I couldn't find a way to soften the situation. How could I soften this reality that now their father had the same thing that took their grandma's life?

The experience that day was very intense, and one I had never thought of having: office, diagnosis, shock, denial, rage, anxiety, fear, unplanned ambulatory surgery, and, finally, breaking the news to my wife and children.

I got home at around seven in the evening. Naomi heard my car and came out to greet me. We embraced and started to cry. Once we calmed down, we went inside.

I asked the children to gather in my bedroom. Naomi made sure that everyone walked in together. They looked at me in shock. "Papi, what happened to you? Did you have an accident? Are you all right?", they asked. I remember their scared faces like it happened today. Alejandro was fifteen years old, Nicholas, thirteen, Thomas and Andres, eleven, and Claudia was only seven years old. Naomi kept her eyes on me, attentive as to how I would tell them the news. I was filled with a power I did not expect I was going to have, and I explained to them what was happening. Perhaps the hardest thing for me was to give the news to my children. Thank God, I had Naomi by my side.

What happened to me? Why? What did I do to deserve this? I felt guilty because I knew that I was not the only one who had to live this situation, but also my wife, my kids, my father, other family members, and my closest friends.

Before I wrote this chapter, I talked to Naomi and with each of my children about those moments when they found out that I had cancer. I asked them if they remembered that night, to share their experience with me.

Naomi was even more scared and shocked than me. She worked in the medical field as an ultrasound and radiology technician and knew about my type of cancer. As my wife, my caregiver and spiritual partner, she was always by my side. I remember praying with her, falling asleep, and waking up again hearing her still praying. This gave me the peace and calmness I needed. As a mother, she had to stay strong for our children and make sure they all prayed together for my recovery. She said, "On the one hand, I told our children to have faith that God would heal me, but on the other hand, I asked myself how our children's faith would be impacted if instead of recovering, I died."

Alejandro, our oldest son, says he pretended that everything was fine, but in reality, he was mad at God for allowing me to get sick. He thought it was unfair for me and the entire family. Claudia remembers when we said goodbye over the phone to her Yaya, the name the children called my mother, as we listened to the song "Let It Be" by The Beatles, and then, as if it were the next day, I was telling them that I was sick with cancer. Thomas, Andrés, and Nicholas tell me that they were very afraid of losing me. They thought that if their grandma had died of cancer, I would also die. Those are the emotions and thoughts that they had when I gave them the news.

In addition to our phone conversation, here is what my son Nicholas wrote:

Hi, Pa.

I am writing to tell you what I felt when you told us about the melanoma that entered your body. We were all sitting in your bed when you gave us the news. I cannot explain the fear I had, and more so after having lost grandma a few weeks earlier. My brothers and Claudia were going to be alone with mom. I always tried to be busy to not think about your cancer. I remember crying while praying for your health and for mom to stay strong, which she always did. They usually tell me that I have a big heart, and it's because of the way you and mom raised us. I do not think I could have better parents than you. I was scared, and I felt empty while you were battling the disease. Now, I am very grateful, and I feel blessed to have you here with us.

I love you, Pa.

About two weeks after my diagnosis, my first procedure was a sentinel biopsy and a lymphatic drainage on the right side of my neck. Due to everything we were going through and the fact that the surgery would be a few weeks later, we decided to go to Disney World the weekend of October 12 to celebrate my birthday. I remember being very anxious and sad, thinking that it could be my last birthday with my family, and I sensed they were thinking and feeling the same. At that time, for me, that was the most important birthday of my life. Every time my kids see a picture of us riding a roller coaster just about to splash in the water at the end of the ride, they say they remember the strange sensation of enjoyment and at the same time being scared of losing their father.

The surgery was successful. Along with the lymph nodes removed, the surgeon extracted a nerve and a muscle to be able to reach lymph nodes. The surgeon removed a total of twenty-three lymph nodes, from which three tested positive for cancer. I started my treatments on December 22, the beginning of what ended up being ten years of remissions and reoccurrences, which progressively got worse.

I must say that the first treatment, scheduled for six months and in which I received interferon alfa 2, was the hardest one of them all. I felt like I was constantly having a strong flu, with chills, strong headaches, bone aches, loss of appetite, nausea, fever, and weight loss. I remember that about two hours after receiving the interferon, I began to shake uncontrollably and had to place myself in bed in a fetal position for at least an hour. Sometimes, I would get such strong stomach aches that I felt they would kill me. Day after day was like that. Doctor appointments, follow-up exams, and blood tests were a physical, mental, and emotional challenge. I went back to work every day, but every hour or so I would lie down to rest. I went to and participated in social and personal events, but they made me anxious and confused. Going to events caused me to repeatedly ask myself "Why me? Everyone is doing their thing, having fun, and I, who should be doing the same, am going through this bitter experience, and I don't even know if I will survive."

I always made the effort to keep working and to go out and maintain my social life, but it was difficult. Most of the time when I went out, my mouth would dry, and I would start getting dizzy and experiencing vertigo. I tried to play tennis, run, or walk, but often I would stop and vomit. The first six months from my diagnosis where horrible, filled with restlessness, malaise, and uncertainty. Sometimes I would accept my situation, sometimes I would get angry at being sick and not being able to live a normal life. I sensed that people around me didn't even remember what I was going through. I worried about my kids, to whom I could not dedicate the same amount of time, which hurt me very much. It hurt me seeing my wife struggling to maintain the same daily routine we had before my disease, and her frustrations when she would realize that she just could not manage. I got into a new vicious cycle of denial, fear, sadness, frustration, physical and emotional discomfort, and acceptance. "When will this stop?", I wondered. "This should not happen to anyone or any family, but it is happening to us." I would say to myself, "Be patient, your treatment ends shortly. The treatment was effective, and you will be back to normal."

It wasn't like that. In the fifth month of treatment, I began to feel a couple of hard lymph nodes on the upper part of the left side of my neck. You cannot imagine how disillusioned I felt. "No way, this can't be happening! The treatment did not work. All this time of struggle, and I did not heal?", I thought. I feared the melanoma was manifesting itself on the left side of my neck, and that's exactly what happened.

Do I have to go through this experience again? Biopsies, diagnosis, anxiety, surgery, and once again discouraging news. The biopsy of one of the lymph nodes came back positive, and my doctors recommended another a radical lymphatic dissection on the left side of my neck. Once again, the surgery was a success. Twenty-two lymph nodes were extracted, from which two where positive, but this time there was no need to extract a muscle or nerve.

"What do we do now doctor? I understand that in most cases chemotherapy does not work on melanoma patients." I searched the internet for other options and found a less toxic treatment. I asked my oncologist if he was aware of the treatment. He told me that it was still in the Food and Drug Administration's approval process, but he said he would check if there was still an opportunity to be included in one of the study groups for that treatment. He was able to sign me up for one of the groups. Luckily for me, I was in the group that was receiving the treatment and not the placebo.

Try to imagine how I felt. I began to realize that no official treatment to fight my cancer type existed.

I was placed on a clinical study for a promising treatment. I received GMCSF (granulocyte and macrophage colony stimulating factor), a peptide that, supposedly, would strengthen my immune system, therefore, would effectively fight the melanoma. I felt like a guinea pig. I began the treatment of self-inflicted intracutaneous shots fifteen days monthly for twelve months, and this time the side effects were minimal. I hoped this second treatment would work because I was feeling much better, and I was beginning to be excited about it.

My friends, living the experience of being a cancer patient is something that I would never wish on anyone, but there are many people dealing with the disease. For those of you who have been diagnosed recently or are currently under treatment, I understand perfectly what you and your loved ones are going through. But I assure you that it is totally possible to overcome your situation, no matter how difficult or the suffering you may be experiencing.

By putting walls around your suffering,
you risk letting it devour you from the inside.
FRIDA KAHLO

Ten in Ten

My journey towards battling the cancer started with the outpatient surgery where the lesion was extracted from the skin on the upper part of my head. A few weeks later, during the process of analyzing the biopsies, the tumor came back in the same spot. After studying the drainage in the sentinel biopsy, Dr. Moffat recommended a radical dissection of lymph nodes on the right side of my neck and told us that he would also remove the tumor that came back on top of my head. As a joke, he told" me he was doing two surgeries for the price of one. I continued with a positive attitude, which certainly helped me stay optimistic. I had exceptional and dedicated doctors for whom I have always thanked God for. They are on the list of angels who took me by the hand.

In November of 2002, I had the second and third surgeries, which consisted of radical dissections. This protocol meant that besides the lymph nodes, if needed, they extract the nerves and muscles.

The doctors extracted twenty-three lymph nodes, of which three were positive, and extracted a nerve and two muscles in the right part of my neck and in my right shoulder. In addition, I was given a catheter for fifteen days to ensure that any lymphatic fluid left in the surgery area could drain properly.

Four weeks later, I underwent interferon alfa 2 treatment to inhibit of the proliferation of cancer cells and activate and strengthen the immune system, which was a literally like having a constant flu. It was a torment, not only for me but for my wife, children, family, and friends.

When someone has cancer,
the whole family and the people
who love him also have it.
pinkrackproject.com

After almost five months of treatment, the melanoma returned to the left side of my neck. Quite logical, because the original tumor was right in the center of the top of my head and Melanoma spreads thru the lymphatic system, meaning it could have drained in either or both directions. Once again, the psychological effects of the diagnosis caused distress to my family and me. The thought of undergoing another surgery caused a great deal of anxiety in me.

I had four surgeries in a period of seven months. Another radical dissection, in which twenty-two lymph nodes were extracted, two of which were positive. Then, we hoped that the new treatment of GMCSF would work: twelve months of daily injections for fifteen days, then I would rest fifteen days, and so on. I had to inject myself in different places of my body to avoid irritations and bruises. During those twelve months, I had four biopsies: two in the right arm, one in the left arm, and another in the right thigh. By that time, I had experienced seven biopsies, and each of them generated the same emotions and anxiety while we waited for the results. The four biopsies came out negative.

In the meantime, in early 2004, a friend who had the same type of cancer that I had, passed away. She was twenty-five years old. Once again, I felt the sting of adrenaline, anxiety, sadness, and fear. This news affected me deeply. My young friend, who studied with joy was to graduate as an architect, while fighting against her melanoma. Once again, I asked, "Why?"

I finished twelve months of treatment without recurrences and of the four biopsies performed, all came out negative. I felt very good. My oncologist suggested that I follow up with the PET (positron emission tomography) scan exam every three months. The year ended, and in the middle of 2005, the doctor reduced my follow- up exams to two per year.

I continued this way through the middle of 2006 when the doctor reduced my follow-up exams to once each year. Everything was going well, until another friend of mine died.

She was another melanoma patient I had met the first day of my treatment. She was only thirty-four years old, and she left her husband and five-year-old daughter.

Once again, I had those feelings and emotions, already so familiar, that this melanoma related news provoked. Once again, I asked, why? Inevitably, I thought about the possibility that eventually I would die. We, as a family, had begun to see the situation as something we had overcome. I was already working, two incomes instead of one made a big difference. It was not easy, it took us while, but everything was beginning to return to normal.

In December 2007, I had an MRI scan in the brain because I was getting frequent migraines, and given my background, the doctors wanted to be sure it was not a melanoma recurrence. The exams went well. But in June 2008, after almost five years in remission, I started having episodes of dizziness, and the strong headaches began to occur more frequently. My children noticed some irregularities in me. They would find me staring at a place, without any reaction, and they had to touch me to get my attention. Naomi realized that I only spoke to her in Spanish, when normally I spoke to her in English. She also noticed that, when talking to one of my clients who just spoke English, in the same way I spoke to him in Spanish. Naomi and my children began to worry, they knew something strange was happening. I started to leave the toothbrush with the toothpaste in the sink; that is, I was intending to brush my teeth, but I did not get to do it. As she noticed these inconsistencies, she became very worried.

One night, when Naomi had gone to her office to print Claudia's homework, I started to stutter when I spoke to the children and I had a very bad headache. Claudia called Naomi and explained what was happening. When Naomi entered the house, she realized that I spoke to her only in Spanish and was stuttering. It was this that convinced her that she should call the oncologist. These symptoms, my symptoms, which I didn't know were happening to me, were the same ones that my mother presented when her lung cancer had affected her brain. This put a burden on Naomi and the kids, since they had been through this with their Yaya before she passed.

Apparently, all this happened to me sporadically, but frequently. Recently, during a conversation with Claudia, she asked me if I remembered the time when she entered the room, worried and scared, and asked me if I was afraid of dying. I told her that I remembered I answered that I was not afraid because that was not going to happen yet, to which she insisted: "How do you know?" I told her that God wanted me to take care of her and her brothers until they were adults. Every time I remember about those times, it hurts me to think that the kids lived a good part of their short lives in fear of losing their father.

The next day, I got up normally and without the slightest idea of what had happened the night before. I bathed and shaved, and we all had breakfast. We were already in our daily routine. Naomi asked me, "Do you feel good?" I replied, "Yes, I do." "Are you going to your client's downtown office?" "Yes."

She offered to take me, which seemed odd. I thanked her and insisted that it was not necessary. In the end, I ended up going alone like any other day. I arrived at my client's office, whom, by the way, were Spanish speaking. I probably was not stuttering yet, since they would have noticed. Everything went smoothly. We ordered our food, and everything went well until we started eating. Suddenly, I looked as if I was hypnotized, looking at my plate without speaking or answering when they asked me if I was okay. When I returned to myself, I told them that everything was fine, but I noticed that their plates were empty and mine only half empty. One of them told me what had happened to me and asked if I wanted to finish eating, but I told him that I was not hungry. We paid and started walking back to the office. I remember that I was walking in the middle, and I had not given importance to that fact, but they had surrounded me as a precaution, considering what had happened in the restaurant. Climbing the elevator, I momentarily lost my sight. My clients noticed my reaction and asked me if I was okay. I told them that I had momentarily lost my vision. They asked for Naomi's phone number and called her to let her know what had happened. Naomi asked them not to let me go. She took the metro rail, picked me up at my client's office in the middle of the afternoon, and took me directly to the oncologist, to whom she explained the situation.

Naomi tells me that I only, only spoke in Spanish even though the doctor spoke to me in English. The doctor asked me how I felt, and I answered in Spanish. He asked me about the date of my birthday, and I struggled to answer, although

I finally did, and the answer was correct. He asked me what day it was, and I answered incorrectly. Finally, he asked me who was our president, and I answered "Ronald Reagan." I vaguely remember sitting in front of the doctor. Naomi told me later that because of my answers, my stuttering, and my behavior, he ordered that I be hospitalized and have an MRI of my brain performed. The next day, they read us the diagnosis of a three-centimeter radius melanoma tumor that was putting pressure on the frontal lobe, the part of the brain that handles our cognitive abilities, such as emotional expression, the ability to solve problems, hold memory, and manage language. This explained my behavior. At noon, they performed another resonance so that the neurosurgeon could specify where to cut to remove the tumor.

We, who had begun to normalize our financial situation, our activities, and our children's lives, had returned to fear, anxiety, and uncertainty. My mountain was full of ups and downs: sometimes the summit seemed to be near, when suddenly a valley appeared. I felt that the mountain of my cancer had just grown impossible to move. I resolved, "Family, we have no other choice but to start over. God is pressing us, but I know he will not choke us."

Never despair, even in the worst moments,
because from the darkest clouds fall
clean and fertilizing water.
Miguel de Unamuno

The next day, early in the morning, I was admitted to the operating room for my fifth surgery, this time a craniotomy that lasted almost eight hours. I must say that in my lucid moments, I felt a lot of fear and worry. In fact, I remember the list of complications that could occur during surgery was truly alarming.

The surgery was successful. They were able to extract the entire tumor, and, miraculously, the only warning the neurosurgeon gave me was that I would probably have a cavity area on the upper part of my forehead, which did not happen. Neither did I have a stroke or motor or speech problems. I felt like I was born again. This time, about four weeks after the craniotomy, I received six weeks of radiation for five days a week. These radiation treatments began to weaken me to such an extent that all I wanted was to sleep after receiving them, and obviously I began to lose my hair.

After four weeks of treatment, I had an MRI of the brain that came out positive with three additional tumors. Due to the size of the tumors, the radiologist recommended the application of Gamma Knife therapy, a radiosurgery procedure that focuses beams of Gamma radiation on one or more tumors but without the inherent risks of conventional surgery. The idea was to eradicate the tumors, which were still small, and finish the two weeks of radiotherapy.

I wondered, "My God! How much more do I have to bear?" This time we decided not to tell the children. They knew that I was receiving radiation therapy, and they had become accustomed to seeing his father without hair and a little thin. I would say that they had surrendered to a cycle of surgeries, treatments, and remissions.

The Gamma Knife, an outpatient surgical procedure, would be my sixth surgery. Since I was not going to be hospitalized, I simply pretended that I was going to one more day of radiotherapy. In my case, it took four hours to apply lasers through a helmet that had been screwed into my head. Yes, they literally screw it up, applying local anesthesia in the places where the special screws, not sharp, would penetrate my skull. The protocol is to follow up a few weeks after the surgical procedure. My radiotherapy ended, and a few weeks later, I had another follow-up resonance. The results indicated that all three tumors had been eradicated. The procedure worked! I was happy to hear that. Maybe I was finally going over the hump.

In the month of March 2009, during a follow-up MRI, three additional tumors appeared, and once again they were small enough to use the Gamma Knife surgical procedure again: my seventh surgery. Again, about six weeks later they performed another resonance, as well as PET (positron emission tomography) scan for the whole body. The results indicated that I had no additional lesions in the rest of the body or in my brain. However, of the three tumors treated with the Gamma Knife, two of them located in the occipital lobe did not reduced in size, and because of their location, they were not operable. The third, located in the left parietal lobe, had increased considerably in size and was approaching the motor area for speech in the brain. The doctor warned us that we had to remove it as soon as possible and probably with local anesthesia to make sure that my speech would not be affected.

Dear reader, as a person of faith, I always tried to see the light at the end of the tunnel, but my hopes were wobbling from the panorama of recurrences in my brain. For the first time, I had inoperable tumors, which caused a lot of anxiety. Denial did not exist. What was happening was too real. I maintained dignity in the face of my situation. Almost seven years into this fight, I was tired and frustrated, but unwilling to give up."

In the realm of ideas,
everything depends on enthusiasm;
In the real world,
everything depends on perseverance.
JOHANN WOLFGANG VON GOETHE

In June 2009, In June 2009, I had a preoperative resonance so that the neurosurgeon could again specify where he would be opening to remove the tumor. The next day, the doctor entered my room with a smile from ear to ear. "Mr. Córdoba, I have two pieces of good news for you. Which one do you want me to tell you first?" It turned out that the medical team in charge of my surgery had had a medical meeting in conference with neurosurgeons at the Anderson Clinic in Houston and concluded that it was not necessary to have a local anesthetic. The second good news was that the two inoperable tumors did not appear in the resonance images. The doctor explained that he would verify this news on the post-surgery MRI.

Once again to the operating room, and once again the anguish and fear for my wife, my children, my father, and my friends. Once again, I risked the possibility of a stroke, and this time there was a risk of affecting my speech. Seven hours in the eighth surgery, and thank God, everything went well, with no stroke or speech problems. Postsurgical resonance verified that the tumor had been extracted in its entirety and that the other two, in fact, had disappeared.

Later on in the book, I share a couple of reflections about the power of faith and prayer, that have a lot to do with this "sudden disappearance" of the two tumors. It felt that I was finally moving my mountain aside, but in the way, I lost two more friends to cancer, and that scared me. I think about my experience during those ten years and how at the beginning I asked, "why me?" As the years passed, and I lost four more of my friends. I asked, "why them and not me?" In the end I began to ask, "For what?"

At the beginning of 2012, during my routine PET scan examination, a tumor appeared deep between the hip and the left gluteus, and after a resonance that verified the position and size of the tumor, I was headed for my ninth surgery, which, due to the location of the tumor, required a long and deep incision through the gluteus. Thank God everything went well. This time they applied a new type of radiotherapy, based on twelve catheters that they inserted through my gluteal so that the radiation could effectively reach the area where the tumor was without affecting my skin. Of the now nine surgeries, this was the most difficult in terms of my recovery because of the wound through my gluteus and the embedded catheters. During the two weeks of radiotherapy, I could not sit down or lie down comfortably. I said to myself that there was still a bit of mountain to move. That's what I thought…

In the month of July 2012, another tiny bug appeared just millimeters from my anus. Can you believe it? Again, to the operating room for another surgery, the tenth one. The surgeon who performed the two surgeries on the buttock and very close to the anus assured me that they would be the last and, thank God, five years later, the doctor was right! No more bugs have appeared!

Ten surgeries in ten years, radio and chemotherapy and innumerable biopsies. This time I can affirm that I was able to move my mountain, but I am clear that in my lifetime there will be other mountains to move, and I will always be willing to move them.

You have been assigned this mountain
to teach others that it can be moved.
ANONYMOUS

Fighting the Opponent

Anyone can give up. It is the easiest thing
in the world to do. But to hold it together
when everyone else would understand if
you fell apart, that's true strength.

CHRIS BRADFORD

I began playing tennis when I was seven years old, and
at the age of ten I started to play tournaments. As a
teen, I became part of the junior national team and
then obtained a la National Colligate Athletic Association
division one college scholarship. As I progressed in the sport
with the help of my teachers and physical coaches, I began
to understand how to study my opponents' strengths and
weaknesses. In my later teens, I was taught relaxation and
visualization techniques to prepare myself mentally and to
improve my chances to win. These techniques helped me
a great deal, and I generally had good results. I studied my
opponents and visualized myself winning.

Playing competitive tennis, especially at a young age,
is not easy because it is an individual sport. I had to overcome challenges, particularly when I would hear talk about
top-seeded players and how hard beating them would be or

comments about how I would have been better off if I had placed on another spot in the draw so that I could win a couple of matches and move further into the later rounds. At times I was feeling run down or sick, but I still had to play my match.

I learned to avoid being negatively influenced by others, or even myself, and just play without fear of losing. If we accept negative affirmations from others, most certainly we will end up building a mental mountain that ultimately becomes an obstacle to reaching goals.

We all have mountains to climb. At the time, my mountain was overcoming the mental obstacles created by my own fears and the influencing affirmations of others toward my playing abilities or about my opponent's abilities. Team sports, which I very much enjoyed as I grew up, were much easier when it came to winning or losing. I could have had played badly on a certain day, but my team could win anyway, or if we lost, we all lost as a group. In the sport of tennis, you either win or lose to your opponent. You are alone on the court. Playing an individual sport is not an easy task to deal with regardless of age.

You may ask why sharing my tennis years history? My answer is, because there is vast similarity exists between what I am describing about tennis and what I was going through with the shock and psychological process of being diagnosed with cancer. I viewed cancer as my opponent. Whether you have experience in sports competition or not, we are all born with an inner competitive survival instinct, and when you are fighting for your life against cancer or anything, that survival instinct kicks in.

This opponent, CANCER, with bold uppercase letters, has quite a reputation. Through the years, this opponent has beaten a few of my relatives and friends, including my dear mother three weeks prior to my own diagnosis. I was very scared. But just like I did as a young boy minutes before I would to step onto the court to compete, I made my mind up to confront this physical, mental, and emotional bully. I was overwhelmed, intimidated, stressed, vulnerable, and worried, but I drew a plan to become as strong as possible against this opponent. I began to look for survivors with similar diagnoses to mine, read books of survival stories, and looked for as many statistics as possible regarding my type of cancer. I thought that the more I knew about this opponent, the better chance I had to prepare myself to win.

I thought that finding other people who came out victorious would be encouraging for me. Those human beings who beat the odds would be my role models and motivation to play the most important match of my life; they would help me believe that I too could come out victorious, that I could move my mountain too. Faith moves mountains.

I found a few advanced staged cancer survivors who were willing to talk and motivate me. We quickly became friends and had a lot in common. Being able to talk with these folks and realizing that they felt what I was feeling helped me a great deal. I was not alone. Others had walked the same road. That definitely gave me a great sense of hope.

Why do think I wrote the word CANCER in uppercase letters? Because most people see cancer as a giant monster that wants to steal their health, dreams, and lives. I was one of them.

When I got sick my oldest son's godmother gave me a wonderful book, There's no Place Like Hope by Vickie Girard, a cancer survivor. Here's a quote from her book that helped me a great deal: "I describe cancer as the word in the entire English language that the mind sees in all capital letters."

Vickie Girard suggests that people see the word in lowercase letters to reduce the size and power of the word. I started visualizing the word cancer in lowercase letters and in a very small font. After all, these tiny little cells cannot be seen with the naked eye. I encourage you to pause for a moment and once again read and absorb the quote from Vickie Girard.

Based on my own experience, I am convinced that the battle is not just physical but also mental, emotional, and spiritual. I believe there is a root cause that triggers cancer, and I am convinced that we have internal and external tools, including family and friends, to help them beat it.

Start with the mind, the single most powerful tool that God designed for human beings. Dr. Joseph Murphy, author of the book The Power of Your Subconscious Mind, says, "Busy your mind with the concepts of harmony, health, peace, and good will, and wonders will happen in your life."

All of us have inner fears, beliefs, and opinions. These inner assumptions rule and govern our lives. A belief has no power in and of itself, its power arises from the fact that you accept it mentally. Dr. Joseph Murphy cites: "As you sow in your subconscious mind, so shall you reap in your body." Our minds are without a doubt a powerful tool and essential for our healing process. Can you visualize cancer in lowercase, and in very small font? Can you see a smooth light beaming health throughout your body cleaning out your illness? Do not worry, there are plenty of exercises to help you sow healing thoughts in your subconscious mind that will share with you later in the book.

Realize as soon as possible that you own your current situation and no one else does. Not your wife, kids, friends, or doctors and nurses. You wake up every morning and deal with your situation. Understand that you are ultimately responsible to regain your health. This is not to say that you do not need people by your side. You certainly do.

Let us replace the words "tennis match" with "fighting cancer." Imagine you are the player and have a team of friends, family, doctors, therapists, nutritionists, spiritual leaders, life coaches, and fellow survivors supporting and cheering to help you win the match. Without doubt they will help and encourage you, but in the end, you are the player who steps on the court to play the match…

The more prepared you are, the better chances you have to win. Worry, anxiety, and fear interfere with the normal rhythm of our hearts, lungs, and other organs and weaken the immune system, which we definitely need to maintain strength for the fight.

If we feed our subconscious with thoughts of harmony,
health, and peace, then all the functions of our bodies
will become normal again.

DR. JOSEPH MURPHY

This stuff may appear to be magical, but I assure you that with practice it becomes natural. To be able to accomplish this a person needs to allow time to retreat, breath, slow down, and relax to become capable to feed the mind with thoughts of harmony, peace, and health. The key is making this a habit, which requires practice. This is the road I chose to walk, and you can take it as well.

There are many guided meditation and relaxation recordings available online that you can use. At the end of the book, I share a few links for you to get started. Remember, set apart ten to fifteen minutes a day to feed positive and healing thoughts and suggestions to your mind. I know it will help you a great deal.

There are other key important components in the quest for health, for example, nutrition.

Throughout my cancer battle I heard many comments about diets and recipes. Suggestions came from friends, family, friends of friends, and colleagues. When it comes to offering advice on foods to eat while ill with cancer, plenty of people are willing to share all about some sort of miracle food or recipe that apparently cures the disease. These comments, though well intended, often contradict themselves.

There is enough information out there to leave a person totally confused. Listen politely and with gratitude to these well-intentioned folks, but please do your own research as well. One thing is certain, your diet is essential for your healing process, and for those who are not ill, an important factor for preventing the disease.

It amazes me how much love and effort people make to keep their plants and pets healthy, yet they don't seem to care about their own eating habits. They learn what is best for their plants and pets, just as they know the type of gas and maintenance their vehicles need for the engine to run well, yet they don't seem to care much about the fuel they put into their bodies.

Because of the unpredictability and stubbornness of melanoma, I underwent several treatments to find what would work best for me. I sensed my wonderful doctors and nurses being in reactive mode, always a step behind the evolution of my disease. The industry was still looking for treatment protocols for melanoma. I underwent, interferon, radiation, and chemotherapy treatments, but these did not work for me. Rather, I felt all that stuff was literally making me more ill with no positive results.

The disease kept coming back. My oncologist and his team, so knowledgeable and dedicated could not find the right formula. I am amazed of how many patients they treat daily and how focused they are in fighting the disease. However, their patient list keeps on growing. I would not wish to be in their position.

What is happening? Is this becoming an epidemic? What can be done? How do we prevent it? What alternatives or complements are there to replace the current forms of treatment? Are their initiatives focused on prevention, rather than reacting when the disease manifests in our bodies?

I was lucky to be treated by incredibly talented and dedicated doctors and nurses, but I began to wonder if we were taking the right approach to overcome my situation. Chemotherapy and radiation still are the popular protocol of choice that help many patients. I am forever grateful for the care I received from them, and I thank God for the surgeons who removed the tumors in my body, particularly those in my brain; without them I wouldn't be here today.

However, I began to feel like a guinea pig after a few years of trying conventional treatments. I concluded they did not work for me. The pattern was surgery then treatment and remission, but it was an exhausting cycle. It was exhausting and I was tired. I did not want to go through this cycle again and again.

I finally tried an alternative approach and went to see an expert offering noninvasive and natural alternatives who, after interviewing and probing me, explained that all diseases originate at the cell level and not at the organ level, and by detoxing our bodies, our cells will begin to return to the natural healthy state which we were designed.

I can say that through nutrition I found a new and powerful way, along with prayer and meditation, affirmations, visualization and a positive attitude to regain health and win the fight.

There are two additional components equally important to our well-being. These are emotions and spirituality.

A few months after I was diagnosed and after my first surgery, I signed up for the weekend retreat called "The Walk to Emmaus" with the intention of bringing my father along. Six months after my mother's passing he was still having a very difficult time coping. Based on the positive comments I have heard about the retreat, and what we were experiencing, that is, mom's death and my diagnosis I figured it would be beneficial to attend.

My intention was to help my dad, but I did not know that this retreat would touch me in such a deep way. Neither did I know that I would end up serving in the retreats that followed, and that eventually I would lead one of them.

In retrospect, after serving and leading in these retreats, I learned that people make plenty of mistakes, often hurting others or getting hurt by the mistakes of others, both being very harmful. We begin to experience mood swings, unhappiness, anger, and regret, which impacts on physical and mental health.

Holding things in can cause a constant state
of elevated stress hormones that the body
is not meant to sustain for long periods of time.
Constantly elevated stress hormones like adrenaline
and cortisol can weaken your immune system.
LISA RENE REYNOLDS

Years ago, I read a book by Daniel Goleman, Emotional Intelligence, which helped me understand how my emotions could control my behavior. When I became ill with cancer and started reading more holistic material, I began to pay much more attention to my emotional state, particularly on its potential negative effects on my health.

The quote mentioned above on "holding emotions" made me heartedly and honestly look inside myself to find the things that happened in my life that caused disruptions and led me to accumulate strong feelings of sadness, anger, and anxiety. I also went deep and analyzed if I have built a mask that prevented me from releasing sentiments to forgive or being forgiven. Where there such sentiments contributing to weaken my immune system that I was holding in and needed to let go. Through silence, prayer and meditation, I began to find the things I have held in and made sure I let them out. I felt as if a heavy weight was removed from my shoulders.

Last but not least, comes the spiritual factor. Many people immediately tie spirituality with religion, but while a religious person may be spiritual, a spiritual person is not necessarily religious. As a Christian Catholic, initially I turned to my parish for prayer and support from my faithful and committed brothers and sisters. As I mentioned earlier, I experienced the Emmaus retreat as well as the Live in the Sprit seminar, a powerful charismatic retreat. I went to several healing masses and prayer groups and several times received the imposition of hands.

At the end, I took all the stuff I read and put it into action. The universal wisdom God conspired and put the puzzle together for me, confirming that when we seek, we shall find.

Understanding that having a coaching and supporting team, owning your disease, and preparing physically, mentally, emotionally, and spiritually are crucial factors for fighting this opponent and regaining your health. Today, I continue to manage my physical, mental, emotional, and spiritual balance, aiming to live a healthy life, and with a purpose, using my time and talents for the collective good of all. Here is my formula: Live in wellness, learning and sharing along the way.

Thank God I am still here. Like all of you, I have no idea when I will go. In the meantime, when I wake up and open my eyes, I give thanks three times: one for my health, one for my family, and one for the opportunity to do one good deed today.

You can be a victim
or a cancer survivor.
The decision is in your mind!
DAVE PELZER

The Healing Process

We were designed to be healthy. We allow the environment and our egos to control our lives and end up abusing our physical body, emotions, and mental health. I recall the exact day I believe my healing process started.

Many ppeople opt to close the door and lock their cancer up inside themselves. I must say that a big part of my healing process was to leave the cancer in my house and go out to do the things I always liked to do, no matter how I was feeling physically, mentally, or emotionally.

During my ten-year battle, I learned many lessons that I have recorded in notebooks and journals written during early morning hours, especially on weekends, while I waited for the sun to rise at South Beach, in Miami Beach.

Throughout repeated reoccurrences and remissions, I have had plenty of opportunities to reflect about family and friends, my responsibility to care for and love this beautiful planet, about the healing experience of helping others from the heart without expecting anything back, and also learning by my own count that miracles do happen when a channel opens between a person who is sincerely willing to give and a person who is sincerely open to receive. When this occurs, we allow God, to perform miracles.

Sadly, many people don't feel comfortable receiving, and oftentimes we end up blocking the healing blessings that are coming our way. Giving is much easier than receiving.

Understanding the importance of taking good care of my body, mind, emotions, and spirit and developing a thankful attitude for the blessings I receive on a daily basis, especially of being alive and healthy; the power of prayer and meditation; being kind and of service to others; and very importantly having learned how to receive and allow others to love and care for me continue to be essential for my health and wellbeing.

When we become ill, we immediately think of a medical doctor and the medicaments available to take our ailments away and bring us back to health. I find it interesting how when we are sick the value of being healthy becomes priceless. Think about a broken bone, a strong flu, a heart attack, or any other ailment of the body. Now imagine when the illness is more severe, for example, being diagnosed with cancer. Everything else becomes secondary: health becomes our most important possession, and we focus on caring for ourselves on a quest to recovery.

Dear reader, if you have been diagnosed with cancer and are in the process of being treated, do not shut the door and hide your situation. Open it and allow people to help you and love you. Allow God and His healing power to flow inward. Allow it to enter your life. Keep in mind that the door of our hearts does not have a knob on the outside. It can only be opened from the inside.

> *Here I am! I stand at the door and knock.*
> *If anyone hears my voice and opens the door, I will*
> *come in and eat with that person, and they with me."*
> REVELATION 3, 20

What I did not expect was that God's love and healing power would be given to me through many people. Allowing others to love and care for you is an essential piece for healing. Love matters; love heals; love is forever. To all of you that gave us (my family and me), love, support and reassurance, thank you.

You are my angels, the main reason I am here today, and I will eternally have a place for you in my heart. Thanks to you, my world is much better. May the light of God shine through me, spreading love, friendship, brotherhood, and healing to you.

- To you, Naomi: Not only did you take care of our children but took care of me just as another son. It still boggles my mind how strong you were, being the only household income while I was ill. What an amazing healing experience praying together every night. I remember calmly falling asleep and occasionally waking up to the sound of your voice still praying for me and our family. Thank you! God bless you!

- To my kids Alejandro, Nicholas, Thomas, Andres and Claudia, my biggest motivation. Thank you! God Bless You!

- To my mother in law, Vina. You practically became my mother after I lost my dear mom. I remember you flying down to our house and spending all your time with us. Your love is second to none. Thank you! God Bless You!

- To you, "Profe Savy", who taught me how to play tennis and compete. You who years later came to watch me play the National Venezuelan Open finals and later invited me to lunch just to give me a book that you said not only would help me win matches and tournaments, but - most importantly - it would help me throughout my adult life. Little I knew that what I learned from the book would help me fight cancer. Thank you! God Bless You!

- To you, Aunt Rufy, who early on bought me an amazing and encouraging book: *There's no place like hope*, which brought me comfort, peace and hope. Thank you! God Bless You!

- To you, Julia, who sent me a beautiful Bromeliad along with a copy of the book *It's not about the bike* by Lance Armstrong, perfectly chosen for me because of my competitive athletic background it gave me motivation to fight the disease. Thank you! God Bless You.

- To you, Aunt Aida, who called me every week from the west coast just to say hi and to tell me you were praying for my healing and for our family (in your morning and evening prayers) and so many times sent us a check from your retirement fund. Thank you! God Bless You!

- To all of you, angels (so many, you know who you are) who brought us cooked food for us and gave Naomi a break. Thank you! God Bless You!

- To all of you, family and friends, who lovingly helped us financially. Thank you! Thank you! God Bless You!

- To you, Juan who knocked on the door early in the evenings just to say that you were stopping by too see how I was and to bring a share of your family dinner. Thank you! God Bless You!

- To you pastors, deacons, brothers and sisters of Mother of Christ catholic church, your faith, love and prayer will forever take a big piece of my heart. Thank you! God Bless You!

- To you, praying warriors, brothers and sisters from North, South and Central America, Spain, Germany and Poland who created an unbelievable and relentless chain of love healing power through prayer. Thank you! Thank you! God Bless You!

- To you, Thomas (Cachorro). We grew up together (from our mothers' wombs), we slept at each other's homes. Thank you for visiting so often, for playing tennis with my boys while I was sick in bed, for taking me to my hospital treatments just to give me company, for being by my side in good times and bad times, for being my friend and brother. Thank you! God Bless You!

- To you, Father Joaquin, who during mass offered the consecration for my healing. The warm feeling flowing through my body was definitely a healer. Thank you! Thank you! God Bless You!

- To you, Stefano, compadre. We grew up together, to you, who cried with me when you finished reading about the severity of my diagnosis on the *New*

England Journal of Medicine, to you who quietly gathered our closest friends and my wife Naomi, to discuss the possibility to help as surrogate families to each one of our kids, for being my friend and brother. Thank you! God Bless You!

- To you, Carlos (Brujita), who stopped your summer camp income to fly to Miami and stay with us for a whole month to help with our day-to-day summer days. For mowing our yard, buying groceries and taking the kids to summer camp, for being my friend and brother. You who practically lived in our house every summer in Venezuela. Thank you! God Bless you!

- To you Gabi, who gave me the Reiki Wellness CD and introduced me to the PH balance nutritionist to help me detox my physical body, never charged for your yoga and meditation classes and invited me many times to take to visit your master. Thank you! God Bless You!

- To you, Fabio (Gabiano), Andre, Stefano, Alaichu, Thomas (Cachorro) and Gabi who collectively purchased and gave us a weekend at a top hotel spa, just when you found out I was diagnosed with Mets in the brain. Thank you! God Bless you!

- To you, Miguel Angel and Mechi, who not only prayed constantly for my healing, but brought me a picture of The Jesus of Mercy which was blessed inside sister Faustina's room in Poland. Thank You! God Bless you!

- To all the doctors and nurses who took care of me, the love and devotion for what you do is one of the reasons why I am still here. Thank you! God Bless you!

- To you Joanna, who gave me love through many free massages, acupuncture and Reiki sessions. Thank you! God Bless you!

You are my angels, the main reason I am here today, and I will eternally have a place for you in my heart. Thanks to all of you, my world is much better. May the light of God shine through me, spreading love, friendship, brotherhood, and healing to you.

A Gift for Life

It's not how much we give but how much
love we put into giving...

MOTHER TERESA

Two generations of tennis players from the Altamira Tennis Club in Caracas, Venezuela had the chance to be taught by Mr. Francios Savy, probably the best teacher in the country. Following in my father's footsteps, I was taught along with many boys and girls by teacher Savy or, as we called him *el Profe*.

In the summer In the summer of 1983, as a junior in college with a tennis scholarship, I traveled to Venezuela to play the National Open Championships. I got to the finals and had to play Freddy Winkelman, a prominent player and one of my role models. Freddy is seven years older than me. Both of us were taught by Mr. Savy, who unexpectedly showed up to watch the match. I was happy and honored to see our dear teacher in the crowd. He came to watch two of his pupils play the National Open Finals. At the time, "El Profe" was the head pro and director at the Tamanaco

Hotel in Caracas. I hadn't seen him in years, and I suppose Freddy hadn't either.

After trailing most of the match, Freddy came back and beat me in five sets, after more than a four-hour match. After the trophy ceremony, the first thing I did was go greet my childhood teacher. I gave him a hug and thanked him for coming to watch our match. He congratulated me for playing at such a high-level match.

A few days after the tournament's final, when I got home in the evening, my grandmother told me that teacher Savy had called and left his phone number for me to please call him back. I was flattered by the fact that he went out of his way to find our home phone number and call. I returned his call the next day, and he invited me for lunch at the Tamanaco hotel. I felt privileged. El Profe was inviting me to have lunch.

Francois Savy was more than a tennis teacher for all of us. He not only taught us to work on the tennis court but gave us advice about life. As young boys and girls we associated his guidance to tennis, but little did we know that later we would end up applying his advice to life.

At lunch, "El Profe" told me that he was impressed with the way I was playing and asked, "The match was yours. You know that, right?" I agreed and expressed that I was a little discouraged for not closing the match in the fourth set.

Then he told me, with his strong French accent: "Yes. You lost the mental battle, but always remember that, winning or losing there is a lot to analyze and learn after playing a match." We talked about my record playing for New Mexico State University, as well as my engineering courses. We had a very nice time.

Just before dessert, he gave me a piece of paper with the title and author of a book and said he would rather give me the book, but he couldn't find it. He insisted I should read it because it was going to help boost my university tennis career, but most importantly it would help in all aspects of my life. The book's title is *The Power of Your Subconscious Mind*, written by Dr. Joseph Murphy.

The cover has the following quote: "This book will give you the key to discovering the immense inner power you have within your reach."

I have read it several times since I bought it in 1983. During my senior year in college, it helped me win many matches just by putting into practice the things I read and learned about visualization. I also learned about the difference between the conscious and subconscious mind. This is a book worth having in your library.

Every night before I went to bed and every morning before starting my daily activities, I relaxed, took a few deep breaths, and began to visualize the things I wanted to happen during my matches, for example, concentrating on the court and ignoring what was happening outside the court. I visualized the end of the match, feeling great for winning and happy for being the victor when I shook hands with my opponent.

I learned not to express negative things about myself while playing my matches. I had to practice these new concepts frequently, but I learned to guide my subconscious mind by saying and thinking constructive thoughts instead of destructive ones.

What I did not know was that what I learned and practiced improving my tennis, was going to be one of the tools, that twenty years later, helped me overcome my illness. Unfortunately, other patients who I met with the same diagnostic lost their fight, lost their match against cancer.

How many times did I win matches I should not have won? I am sure that a good part of my miraculous healing was due to these mental exercises of visualization and feeding positive words and thoughts to my subconscious mind.

When I was diagnosed with cancer and finally accepted my situation, I realized that this was another match with different types of opponents. In this case it was not about winning or losing a tennis match; it was about winning or losing my life.

I remembered "El Profe" telling me that learning and applying the principles of Mr. Murphy's book would not only help me with my tennis but in all areas of my life. Shortly after my diagnosis, that was exactly what I did. I started to prepare myself as well as I could physically and mentally to fight this opponent called cancer. I read everything I could about detoxing my body and adopting healthy nutrition. I read motivating cancer survival stories. I exercised. I read the highlighted areas of Mr. Murphy's book and put into practice everything I was learning regarding the body, mind, emotions, and spirit to beat my new opponent.

From a mental point of view, I want to share the exercises I practiced up to four times a day while I was in the middle of my battle with cancer. I still do these today at least once a day. I look for a place of silence where I will be free from interruptions. I lie on the floor on a yoga mat or sometimes on my bed or on a sofa in my office and stretch and breathe to clear my mind of thoughts. I close my eyes and begin focusing on my breathing for a few minutes then I begin to visualize a blue healing light entering through my head and expanding throughout my body to my feet, passing through my bones, muscles, and organs, cleaning and eliminating everything that is not healthy. In other occasions I imagine this light becoming Pac-Man and eating any substance or cell that is not good for me. When I was sick, I repeated it several times a day. I found an appropriate place where I could be quiet for about fifteen minutes. Sometimes I could not lie down, so I would sit in a straight meditation posture with my eyes closed.

One of the teachings that has stuck with me from the first time I read *The Power of Your Subconscious Mind* was the explanation about how the conscious and subconscious mind works. Dr. Murphy uses as an example the relationship between a ship captain who, from the upper deck (the conscious mind), instructs the sailors in the engine room (the subconscious mind), and how as the sailors receive the instructions they blindly obey and act upon the captain's orders. I understood that, as a captain of my own ship, I could send positive or negative messages to my sailors, and they would act accordingly upon those orders. This was like discovering a treasure hidden inside of myself. This is what Jesus meant by "ask and you shall receive." It is true, if you send the message that you can't do it, you certainly will not be able to do it, but if you send an absolute "yes I can", without a doubt you will be one of the x% of cancer survivors.

I understood the intention of my dear Profe when he recommended the book, and I will always be grateful for his willingness to share it with me to discover this secret he once found and payed forward to me and many of his pupils.

If you receive something you know can help others, you must share it cheerfully and ask the receiver to do the same. Can you imagine what would happen if everyone practiced this? We would live in a much better world.

My Profe had a sincere intention to give me the opportunity to help myself not only improve my tennis but all aspects of my young and future life, and I accepted his gift with faith and gratitude.

If we truly have the intention and disposition to help someone, and this person accepts and receives with gratitude, a channel opens where undoubtedly God performs miracles.

I thank Profe for his sincere intention to guide me and share this secret. This book not only helped me to improve my tennis, and in many occasions, win matches I should not have won, but ended up helping me beat the toughest opponent I have ever confronted.

Thank you Profe, for this gift for life, thank you from the bottom of my heart.

Blessed is the one who gives
and does not remember,
and the one who
receives and does not forget.
ANONYMOUS

Forgiving is Healing

Forgiveness does not change the past, but it does enlarge the future.

PAUL BOESE

We have all been hurt by another person's action at some point in time. We have been treated poorly, our trust has been broken, or our hearts have been hurt. To feel pain is natural, but sometimes we hold on to it for too long. Identifying with the pain makes us unhappy and creates a chain reaction that eventually ruins our relationships. The unhappiness that comes from our attachments to the feeling of pain blocks us from being open to new experiences, and in most cases, it leads to illness.

When we hold onto the feeling of pain, we trap ourselves in a vicious cycle that alternates between being hurt and being angry. In this state, we miss out on the beauty of life. We need to forgive, whether the person who caused us harm is repentant or not. By forgiving, we can move on and be happy. Forgive and let go…

Forgiveness does not mean
accepting the wrong
doing of the other person,
but to retain a feeling of anger,
hatred, or stress
does more harm to yourself
than the act of forgiving.

The real meaning of forgiveness
is to mentally
not develop feelings
of anger and hatred
due to the wrong action of others.
DHALAI LAMA

The Dalai Lama tells us that if we harbor negative feelings, it will affect our behavior and bring more negativity into our lives. This cycle takes us deeper into a state of unhappiness. To forgive our aggressor does not mean we accept their past behavior. It means we are no longer willing to hurt ourselves emotionally, mentally, and physically, by holding the destructive feeling of anger in our hearts. Perhaps the only reason for us to forgive is to preserve our own state of health.

*Holding onto anger is
like drinking poison and
expecting the other person to die.*
BUDDHA

There are many writings and illustrations about forgiveness in the Holy Scriptures of all religions, and in the writings of enlightened people. They all seem to indicate that forgiveness has the power to liberate and heal. If we know that forgiveness is liberating and healthy, then why is it so difficult to forgive? I believe it's a matter of humility. Our ego tells us to wait for the other person to come and forgive us, instead of us going to ask them for their forgiveness. But time keeps passing and the more time that passes, the heavier and more damaging the load becomes.

After years of feeling anger toward a loved one, I realized that I needed to be forgiven as well. As my health condition worsened and things became uncertain, we finally embraced and forgave each other. We cut the chains and liberated ourselves of a weight that we could have stopped carrying long before.

Our relationship improved, and it helped me become happier. Being happy, is being healthy. I was not aware of the negative consequences the anger had brought into my life. This may be pure coincidence, but ever since I began to forgive, the melanoma had not come back.

When we forgive, past memories do not vanish, nor will our aggressor change his or her behavior. By forgiving, we let go of the anger and pain. On the other hand, when we hurt other people, we also carry a heavy burden that is detrimental to our health. If you are sorry for your actions, I recommend talking to the person and asking them for their forgiveness. This will liberate you. It will be up to the other person to forgive you or not, but your consciousness will be clean. If you are not forgiven, the load will drop on the person you hurt. Giving and receiving, forgiving and being forgiven are experiences that can open a channel to the love of God for your wellbeing.

This is certain: a man that
studies revenge keeps his wounds green,
which otherwise would heal and do well.
JOSIAH BAILEY

We are responsible for our actions and thoughts. Stop recalling hurtful memories, let them become scars and choose to be happy. All of us have the capacity to forgive. We simply have to be humble for our own good.

For everyone who raises himself up
will be humbled,
and the one who humbles himself
will be raised up.
LUCAS 14: 11

Now what if you wish to forgive someone, or ask for their forgiveness, but that someone is no longer living? How may you heal those memories and liberate yourself? An effective way is to request their forgiveness or offer them your forgiveness through prayer. Then, find someone you trust and respect, explain your situation, and pray together so that he or she may act as a surrogate. By doing this you can experience the healing benefits of forgiving or being forgiven by someone that is no longer living. This is a powerful experience that can aid in your healing. It really works!

I am a witness to the power of forgiveness. It broke the jail I had built around my own self. It wasn't about the aggressor, it was about opening the gate and stepping out of my self-built cage. It was about unloading the toxic waste I had been carrying for years. Forgiveness allowed me to move forward and empower my healing process.

I just saw a wonderful movie, *October Baby*. I strongly recommend watching it. It is a beautiful example of the liberating power of forgiveness.

Dr. Steven Standiford, chief of surgery at the Cancer Treatment Centers of America said at an interview with CBS, "Un-forgiveness is classified in medical books as a disease. Refusing to forgive makes people sick and keeps them that way". Forgiveness therapy is now being used to help treat diseases, such as cancer. It is important to treat emotional wounds because they can hinder someone's reactions to treatments, even someone's willingness to pursue treatment.

According to research by Dr. Michael Barry, "of all cancer patients, 61% have problems related to forgiveness, and of those, more than half are grave. Harboring these negative emotions, this anger and hatred, creates a state of chronic anxiety," he said. "Chronic anxiety, very predictably produces excess adrenaline and cortisol, which deplete the production of natural killer cells, which is your body's foot soldier in the fight against cancer." He goes on to explain that, "The first step in learning to forgive is to realize how much we have been forgiven by God."

Dear reader, I wish from the deepest part of my being that you have received my message. There is great power in forgiveness: it is the power of healing and liberation.

To forgive is to set a prisoner free
and discover that the prisoner was you.
LUIS SMEDES

Service

The best way to find yourself is to lose yourself in the service of others.

MAHATMA GANDHI

When I was 17 years old, finishing my senior year in high school, I was invited to join a group of 16 students and 2 Champagnat Marian brothers. Together, we went on a seventeen-day mission to help the Guajiro Indians who live on the Venezuelan/Colombian border. The mission involved cutting though heavy vegetation with machetes, to create enough space to build more houses in their small town and help to install electricity in their homes.

We stayed in an old colonial house where we slept in hammocks with mosquito netting for protection. The bathrooms were holes in the ground with septic tanks underneath, each hole was separated by wooden boards for privacy. Every afternoon, when we were done working, we bathed in the river.

This was a big change compared to the lifestyle we knew in the city of Caracas, Venezuela. Nonetheless, for those of us who volunteered on this mission, it was a unique experience. Living with the Guajiros for seventeen days, sharing around a campfire every night, attending daily mass together, simply spending time in their village, made this mission a powerful and positive influence in my young life.

The wholeness one feels when helping others without expecting anything in return cannot be described. It was not easy, it required discipline and will. But in the end, I felt there was something unknown inside me that had always been waiting to come out. My fellow volunteers shared similar feelings and also felt the same joy. I will always be grateful to Brother Carlos for gifting us this life experience, which introduced us to the love of God manifested in through service. From that missionary journey forward, I have always been willing to help and serve others. In fact, helping others was one of the factors that contributed to the healing during my battle against cancer. By serving others I began to feel God close to me.

Service is an important component in our lives. It is a talent given by God to all humans! Whether you are rich or poor, healthy or sick, no matter your age, race, or culture, if you are not serving others, there is no doubt that you have a void that needs to be filled.

The only happy people are
those who have learned to serve.
ALBERT SCHWEITSER

Whether you are sick or not, being happy promotes health and serving others makes us happy. Looking back at the course of my life, I can see that my happiest moments were when I was helping others. Especially when I was sick. I didn't know it then, but I was being rewarded. I felt better physically, emotionally, spiritually and mentally. Serving others helped me to heal. It seems that there was a divine formula, a hidden gift that orchestrated love and healing. Serving others works wonders in all areas of your life.

I remember praying to God and asking him to give me a little more time to be with my family, and to put my faith into action by helping others. He granted my request and here I am, fifteen years later. Since then, he has given me the opportunity to serve others in spiritual retreats and prayer groups. Also, through the voluntary Road to Recovery program, sponsored by the American Cancer Society, as well as the "Kindred Hospice" volunteer program, and visits to the social services shelter for children under seven years of age. Most of my work began when I was struggling with my illness, and that is why I write about service with such conviction.

My dear friend, when you serve, the feeling has to come from the heart, it has to be genuine and without expectations, and I assure you that you will feel the presence of God.

If you want to know the love of God,
you must descend into the hearts of those you serve.

Jaime Jaramillo

(better known as *papá Jaime*, who has dedicated
himself to helping street children in Bogotá, Colombia)

Throughout the ages, many teachers have spoken of the power of service. Practicing what they preached, they developed personal relationships with the people they served. In the moment of giving and receiving when both, the one who gives and the one who receives, experience the universal love of God. His love is healing. What a wonderful truth!

Be mindful that you do not limit yourself to serving only your family. Obviously, everything starts at home! But the key to the power of service is in serving beyond the duties and responsibilities of our family.

Giving happiness to others
is tremendously important
to our own happiness,
and a most satisfying experience.

Some people think of their own family:
"us four and no more."
Others think only of self:
"how am I going to be happy?"
But these are the very persons
who do not become happy!

To live for self is the source of misery.
In being of spiritual, mental, and material
service to others,
you will find your own needs fulfilled.

As you forget self in service to others,
you will find that, without seeking it,
your own cup of happiness will be full.
PARAMAHANSA YOGANANDA

Dear brother or sister, who is affected by cancer, I challenge you to leave your illness at home as often as possible. I challenge you to find ways to do the things you have always liked to do. But, please go out to into the world help others. Giving is healing. Through service, the void and loneliness that may have contributed to your current situation is filled. In my case, serving others definitely aided my healing process. There are so many things we can do for others in such simple ways, and in turn, our wellness cup will begin to fill up.

Rivers don't drink their own water;
trees don't eat their own fruit;
the sun doesn't shine for himself,
and flowers don't spread their fragrance
for themselves.

To live for others is nature's rule.
Life is good when you are happy;

but you will be much better when others
are happy because of you!!!

Our nature is to serve:
he who doesn't live to serve,
constantly experiences an emptiness.
UNKNOWN

Stop and Smell the Roses

I aim to find the pleasure of re-capturing the limbo of the time that is slipping away and the days that are passing by, I want to feel, I want to walk, I want to paint and perceive the color of the flower that one day will wilt.

MANOLO GARCÍA
(member of El Último de la Fila)

Unfortunately, most people in this world seem to die before they find their purpose and do the one thing, they say they want to accomplish. Time slips away quickly, and before we know it our dreams never come true, and our life purpose is never fulfilled.

Today, I am a volunteer in an organization dedicated to providing support to people in hospice care. When I visit and talk with them, I ask myself, "What would they answer if I asked them if they fulfilled their purpose in life? Will they tell me that they wasted most of their years?". In his book, *Who Will Cry When You Die?* Robin Sharma points out that most people die at twenty but are buried at seventy or eighty. What happens in the middle?

We somehow stop dreaming, begin doing things to make others happy, and we get caught up in our daily routines and adjust to how society dictates how we ought to behave. So, in our twenties we stop living.

A few years ago, as a volunteer for the Road to Recovery Program of the American Cancer Society, which transports cancer patients to and from their treatment sites, I had the privilege of meeting and driving a wonderful woman.

The American Cancer Society has a staff that calls volunteers to coordinate the rides between volunteers and patients. They are trained to call volunteers who best match with the patient address. However, for this ride it wasn't the call center that called me, but the Dade County program director. She told me she received an unusual request from the Homestead/ Monroe County office and immediately thought of me. She gave me the details. This person was flying to New York to start a new and promising experimental treatment that apparently had very good results on patients with her condition. She also said that this patient had to stop driving because she began to lose her sight due to the amount of radiation treatments to her brain. The director explained that this ride was not typical, that it would cover three south Florida counties to get her to the Fort Lauderdale Airport.

The ride coincided with the first day of school, and our five children were attending three different schools. My wife and I had to split morning routes to drive the kids to school.

My first thought when the program director started talking about this ride on the phone was why did she called me. I explained to her about our new morning schedule, justifying why I could not commit to this drive request. However, I had an intuition that I was supposed to accept this drive. maybe there was a higher reason why I was called.

I agreed to drive her to the airport knowing that my wife and I would solve the school transportation problem. I took note of her address, telephone number, and detailed directions because it wasn't easy to get it. We were able to solve the school transportation issue for that morning, it all worked out as if this ride was planned weeks ahead of time for me.

Because of her flight departure time, we had to be at the airport by 5:30 a.m. The drive from her home, in Homestead, to the Fort Lauderdale airport in Broward County typically took more than an hour. At the time I lived in West Kendall, in Miami Dade, and this patient's home was about twenty miles south of my house. I figured that the trip would take me an hour and forty-five minutes to drive down to Homestead, pick her up, and drive north to Fort Lauderdale. I woke up at three thirty in the morning to make sure I had plenty of time to get her to the airport on time.

I was sipping my coffee, driving south on the Florida Turnpike. Halfway to her home I thought of reviewing the directions. To my surprise, I left the instructions and my cell phone home on my kitchen counter. I did not have time to turn around and go back home, so I had to rely on my memory.

I remembered it was the fourth house on the right of the street, as well as the avenue number. Amazingly, I got there on time without directions without missing a turn, just as if I had driven to her house many times.

When we give with a joyful heart without expecting anything back, things flow just right.

I made my last turn and began to count the homes to my right, and I noticed someone was already out on the sidewalk with a carryon bag and a small suitcase. Of course, this was my passenger, who later told me that she had decided to come outside to make sure I did not miss the house because there were no streetlights and it was pretty dark.

She was very friendly, in her mid-thirties. I stepped out of the car, we introduced ourselves, and I placed her luggage in the trunk.

One of the rules of the Road to Recovery Program is not talking about the patient's condition until the patient does, and by no means should volunteers offer medical advice or special diets. I was notified about this ride just the day before. I was told that the first person they thought of for this special case was me. This program is structured by south Florida counties and this ride crossed three of them, and I was able to resolve the first day of school transportation situation without setbacks.

Everything happened as if this ride was planned well in advance. My rider was very talkative and courteous. I learned about her two engineering degrees. She was from the state of Maine and accepted a job in Florida primarily because she loved gardening and wanted to live in a place where she could plant and maintain her flowers, especially roses, because she loved roses. She talked about everything, as if we were best friends.

She told me she had been fighting cancer for some time. It started on her breast and had spread to her liver and brain. Despite the wear and tear from all the treatments and surgeries she looked very pretty and carried herself with dignity. My new friend had practically dedicated her adult life to her schooling and professional career, leaving little time for friends and family.

It was an unforgettable ride. In fact, it seemed we had known each other forever. We had an opportunity to talk about many things: people's personalities, our careers, priorities and families, cancer, her diagnosis, my diagnosis, nutrition, God, faith, world religions, life, and death.

She knew she did not have much more time, and her New York trip, to supposedly receive a new innovative treatment, was just her excuse to go to Maine to be with her family, particularly her sisters and young nieces whom she had not met due to her busy schedule.

In her own words, "I am just trying to hang on just to meet the new ones in the family." My dear friends, the little things she talked about are huge.

As I was fighting my own gloomy statistics, I remember praying to God for the chance to see and be part of my daughter Claudia's first communion, as well as the opportunity to see my boys graduate from high school.

No prejudice exists when a person is dying. Short, tall, rich, poor, black, white, yellow: we will all go one day. We see it every day in the news, especially when a famous person dies. Actors, musicians, business icons, religious leaders, friends and family, your gardener, and your doctor, some with amazing talents, others with lesser talents, but the fact that one day each of us will die is a sure thing.

I mentioned before that my new friend's hobby was gardening, which she focused on more after she found out she was ill. She mentioned she simply planted more roses and asked her neighbor to water them while she was out of town. She loved reading, but her vision was compromised from all the radiotherapy applied to her head. She said that she was a workaholic and regretted missing much precious time with her family. "And what for?", she reflected.

As we drove north toward the airport, we shared more regarding the things we missed as we are distracted with other stuff. For example, how many sunsets and sunrises had we gotten to witness in our lifetimes? We agreed that if we were to ask most people, they would be able to count them with the fingers of one hand.

I narrated the experience that I had on a cool Sunday morning, while I was sitting in my sleeping bag waiting for the sunrise on the beach in South Beach, when I noticed a person lying down about twenty feet away from me completely covered with a blanket and a baseball cap. It was still dark. My first thought was that this person was one of the many homeless around South Beach. Maybe he or she would be sleeping comfortably, under a peaceful night on the shores of Miami Beach.

Just a few minutes before the sunrise, the person sat up and pulled a journal out of his backpack and started to write. I was also writing on my journal, but I continued to be curious about my neighbor.

Suddenly when the temperature started to warm up, he took off his cap and sweater and to my surprise he had a cancer survivor shirt from an event called "Relay for Life", an American Cancer Society fundraising event in which I had participated. I was wearing the same shirt that morning. Coincidence? Perhaps, or as Carl Jung labeled it, a synchronicity.

Incredible, what were the chances for anything like that to happen? Was this a message? How coincidental was that? The only other person around at that time, practically sitting next to me, contemplating the sunrise was another cancer survivor, and he was wearing the same shirt I was wearing.

I shared this experience with my new friend and spoke about this apparent fateful coincidence. Humans tend to ignore the beauty and miracles around us until we are shaken by a life-threatening experience.

We agreed that most people are stuck in their daily routines. Maybe in traffic, thinking about their work responsibilities while they drive to the office or about dinner or other tasks while they return home in the afternoon. Maybe when they arrive, they sit down and watch television for a few hours or talk to someone on the phone. Every morning they struggle to get a few more minutes of sleep. People are just too tired to wake up a few minutes earlier and keep quiet in their thoughts or to be thankful for everything they have, prepare for what waits for them that day, witness the first rays of light beaming through the leaves of a tree, or just listen to the birds and get in tune with nature while taking a short walk.

As we were approaching the airport, she said, "Yes, Georges, I love gardening! I think it is what has kept me going, and I think I have very little time left to do it. Who is going to take care of my garden? If I had a chance to offer a piece of advice to the world right now, I would tell them to stop and smell the roses, to appreciate and enjoy life while they have time."

I never had the chance to see my new friend again. She never returned to South Florida to work on her garden, but I am sure she had a chance to fertilize the hearts and souls of her dear family.

For me, that morning ride with my new friend made me feel I was the person who was being helped, not the helper. I often think about that morning, and when I do, it reminds me that I do not want to be one of those people who dies in their twenties but is buried in their seventies or eighties.

I simply do not know why I was so lucky to survive. I just know that while I am here, I will challenge myself to enjoy, care for, and share this beautiful world. I embrace the sunrise, the sunset, the fool moon, the mountains and forests. I connect with mother earth. I "Stop and Smell the Roses".

In memory of Katherine Green-Bates

Letter to Stephanie

Dear Stephanie, how are you? Thank you very much for your letter. I am very happy to hear from you. Your words have made me cry with joy and love. I am very happy that you and your family were able to share with your wonderful sister.

I feel fortunate and grateful for having the opportunity to drive Katherine to the Fort Lauderdale airport as a volunteer of the American Cancer Society's Road to Recovery Program, during such a special morning. Without a doubt, everything happens for a reason.

Despite having barely met, that wonderful morning we had a very deep and open conversation. It was a blessing for both of us. I think I could have taken her on Interstate I-95 north to New England. The trajectory to the airport seemed very short, but we had the opportunity to share a lot in such a short time. I am convinced that we had to meet.

I am writing a book about the blessings that came to my life from having been diagnosed with cancer, and one of them was to meet Katherine. I wrote a chapter about my meeting and conversation with your sister. As you know, she loved gardening, and particularly growing roses, so I titled the chapter "Stop and Smell the Roses." I will send you a copy as soon as I publish the book.

Katherine knew she did not have much time left, but her acceptance was admirable. Her attitude was very humble, or as she put it: "a proud woman who at the end realized that her life should not have been centered around her profession".

I am glad you found me and wrote me because as we embraced in a goodbye hug at the airport, she told me she was not going up to New York for the new chemotherapy treatments, she truly wanted to spend time with all of you in Maine. I was wondering how I could get in touch with a close family member, and I received your letter.

Toward the end of her days, all Katherine wanted to do was to be close and share with her family. She told me that maybe she could do a little gardening in her sister's yard. Katherine expressed that her two college degrees and PhD meant nothing to her. She said, "if only I could have known this before."

When it comes to giving and receiving, God works in mysterious ways. As a volunteer of the Road to Recovery Program, I left my house very early in the morning, thinking I was driving another patient to treatment. But, just like in most of the cases, what happened was that I received a lot from

Katherine as well. It was such a powerful connection that only God could have planned.

In such a short time, two people who have never met before shared so much and so openly. It was something incredible. One of the topics we talked about was related to miracles, which typically occur when a person is willing to give with an open heart and another person is open to receive. In a mystical way, I believe that miracles happened for both of us that day. We connected in such a way, that only could have happened by the grace of God. It was truly a blessing meeting Katherine.

You may ask yourself: what was the miracle? Well, Katherine and I grew up in different countries, we lived in different states, we met in South Florida, and, in just one and a half hours, we got to share openly and profoundly and became great friends.

The book will be titled *Good Morning, Sunrise*, as soon as it is published I will send you a copy.

I wish you the best. God bless you.

With love,

GEORGES

Faith

Because of the littleness of your faith; for
truly I say to you, if you have faith the size of
a mustard seed, you will say to this mountain,
'Move from here to there,' and it will move;
and nothing will be impossible to you.

MATTHEW 17: 20

Nothing will be impossible to you". That is an em-
powering phrase. Just by having a little bit of faith,
as little as a mustard seed, one of the smallest seeds
in nature, nothing will be impossible to you. Jesus uses this
metaphor to explain the power of faith. A little tiny bit of
faith can move a mountain. Does this mean that with just
a little faith, I can move my mountain, which today, is my
illness?

I have had several mountains to move aside through
my life, the biggest one was advanced cancer. No matter
what mountain you are facing right now, you certainly can
move it aside. Yes, my friend, you can move your cancer
mountain as well.

Have you ever woken up in the middle of the night
and been unable to go back to sleep, then spent a long
time forcing yourself back to sleep? I am not talking about

waking up because you need to go to the bathroom or because you have a cold, a headache, or a physical injury that interrupts your sleep. I am talking about opening your eyes and feeling wide awake in the middle of the night when everyone else is sleeping. This happened to me, occasionally, since I was a boy. But when I was sick with cancer, it happened almost every night, usually at around three a.m.

I would twist and turn, lie on my back and on my belly, thinking about my situation, wondering what would happened to Naomi and our five children, how much longer I could sustain working full time, and many other anguishing thoughts. I would get out of bed, making sure I did not wake Naomi, and peeked into each child's room, watching them sleep. I was confused with the contradiction of being blessed with a beautiful family, but on the other hand fighting an aggressive form of cancer that could end it all for me. Most of these nights I would stay awake, sitting in the living room for a few of hours, restlessly thinking until dawn.

Since I was up so early, I started going to seven thirty in the morning mass before heading to my office. These daily masses worked wonders on my soul, my spirit, my emotions, and my mental attitude. In that half an hour I managed to get rid of everything and focus on the liturgy, waiting with longing for communion, during which I thanked God for all the blessings he was granting me: my children, wife, my family, friends, and work.

One morning after mass, one of the women who regularly attended the morning mass approached me as I was leaving the chapel. She introduced herself and asked me if I could do her a big favor. I said, "Sure Miriam, how can I help you? What can I do for you?". She asked me if I was waking up in the middle of the night due to my situation. She said that it was a normal reaction to be anxious and scared, that even Jesus as a man also felt that way in his moments of uncertainty. I nodded my head in agreement.

The favor she asked of me was to take advantage of the time I was awake in the silence of the night and open my Bible and read about Jesus' miracles. I conceded and told her that I would do it next time I woke up.

That same night, just as almost every previous night, I woke up at 3:00 a.m. I got out of bed and initiated what now seemed to be a routine: watching Naomi sleeping and walking the hall to watch the children, but this time, instead of sitting down and thinking about my situation, I picked up the Bible and did exactly what Miriam asked me to do. I randomly opened the latter pages of the new testament and the first thing I read was the miracle of the woman who had been subject to bleeding for twelve years. She had suffered a great deal for years and had spent all she had to be cured, yet instead of getting better, she actually got worse. Once she heard about Jesus, she decided to be part of the crowd. As the master was passing by, she came up from behind and touched his mantle because she thought, "If I just touch His clothes, I will be healed." Immediately after touching Jesus' mantle, her bleeding stopped, and she felt she was freed from her suffering.

Jesus recognized the amount of energy that came out from him. He turned around in the crowd and asked, "Who touched my clothes?", "You see the people crowding against you," his disciples answered, "and yet you ask, 'Who touched me?'" But Jesus kept looking around to see who had touched him. Then the woman, knowing what had happened to her, walked out and fell at Jesus' feet with fear and told him the truth. He said to her, "Daughter, your faith has made you well. Go in peace." (Luke 8:48)

After reading about this miracle, something clicked in me regarding faith. I kept looking for miracles in the new testament and again, Jesus repeated, your faith has healed you. He never said I healed you or that God has healed you, he said, then and now, that it is our faith that heals us.

Before my conversation with Miriam, who I consider one of the angels that God sent to help me through my process, I would wake up and inevitably start thinking and living my situation for hours, but from the night I woke up and opened the Bible to look for Jesus' miracles. I began to look forward to waking up in the silence of the night to read spiritual and uplifting books and articles. Little by little, I began to pray and meditate.

Rather than feeling anxious or stressed, I began to feel calm through prayer and meditation, in silence, spending time with God. Now, waking in the middle of the night was like I had an appointment with Jesus in my living room to receive what I needed to heal. When I say "heal," I mean experiences that I had carried inside of me for years, causing resentments, regrets, and guilt, components that I believe contributed to my illness.

Have you ever thought that waking up in the middle of the night may be your soul's desire to be awake, the longing for silence impossible to find during your daily routine in a fast paced, anxious, and loud world? Slow down, where are you going, why so fast? If you think you don't have time to rest and retreat because of your daily routines, think about those likeminded souls whom have been diagnosed with cancer and find themselves obligated to slow down.

If you are currently under cancer treatment or if you have been recently diagnosed, I know that you probably have not had a good night of sleep unless you have been taking prescribed sleeping pills. Next time you wake up, get up out of bed, go to your favorite place in your home and sit in silence and enjoy the experience of being in silent solitude. Do not force your way back to sleep or take an extra sleeping pill. Instead, try to see it as an opportunity to connect with God, who longs for you to open the door of your heart so that he can come in. Human beings try to understand God as an external entity, but he is within us and cannot be seen.

Now faith is confidence
in what we hope for and
assurance about what we do not see.
HEBREWS 11, 1

For me this is not an easy task, because oftentimes I leave that place of silence and allow the noise that is around my daily life to take me from the silence of my heart to the noise in my mind, and I begin to think and act according to what society wants. My consolation is that this is also true for the mystics of all religions, who, of course, strived to maintain the confidence and security of their faith.

Going back to spiritual books and articles, I found out that when he was alive, Jesus had moments of doubt. Mother Teresa of Calcutta had her moments of doubt as well. A woman with saint qualities, she was, however, a human being like us. She was a compassionate person dedicated to the welfare of those she served. She held the hands of people while they were dying and hugged, kissed, and fed hungry people. She attended the needy with her own hands, while showing an eternal smile that reflected her love. However, she often had moments of emptiness, weariness, and confusion in which she doubted herself, her ministry, her purpose, and her own faith.

Where is my faith? – even deep down, right in,
there is nothing but emptiness & darkness.

My God, how painful is this unknown pain.
It pains without ceasing. I have no faith.
I dare not utter the words
and thoughts that crowd in my heart
and make me suffer inexpressible agony.

So many unanswered questions live within me
I am afraid to uncover them because of the blasphemy.
If there is a God, please forgive me.
MOTHER THERESA

Many mystics have had these dark moments of desolation and doubt. It is normal to doubt or fear that things will not happen like you want as you are trying to move your mountain, fighting your disease. However, you must keep trying. Remember, miracles happen because of faith. God is waiting for us to call him in prayer and to visit him in the silence of our hearts. He will give you the confidence that will heal you.

Have you ever met the pilots that fly the airplanes you board when you go on vacation or a business trip? Do you have an idea of who they are or if they live a healthy or stressed life, have family problems, had a good night sleep, or have a drinking or drug problem? Or, do you trust that these unknown people you have never seen will safely take you to your destination? Unconsciously, you have faith that everything is going to be okay. So, what is the difference? Why not having faith in God, who takes care of the flowers in the fields and the birds in the sky? How much more would God care for you? For me, it came to a point where I surrendered my cancer situation to God and faithfully in whom I placed all my trust.

For with God nothing
shall be impossible.
LUKE 1: 37

Trusting in God is easier when things seem to be going well for us. Telling someone else to trust God is easy but believing that when the situation is your own gets much tougher. This happens because most people do not have the time to stop to embrace the necessary silence and solitude required to feel God's presence and the confidence that He provides.

To trust God in the light is nothing,
but to trust Him in the dark is everything.
ANONYMOUS

Begin with accepting what is happening,
letting go of what happened,
and have faith in what will happen.

Our egos produce the insecurity
that makes this hard.

Absolute unquestioning faith in God
is the greatest method of instantaneous healing
An unceasing effort that arouse that faith
is the highest and most rewarding duty.
PARAMAHANSA YOGANANDA

Faith heals our emotions, our wounds memories, our bodies, and our souls. The next chapter explains more about the power of faith through prayer and how it worked for me.

Prayer

Prayer is not asking. It is a longing of the soul. It is daily admission of one's weakness. It is better in prayer to have a heart without Words than words without a heart.

MAHATMA GANDHI

I remember sharing my testimony at a Christian stewardship seminar about how important prayer was throughout my healing process and how I had not stopped praying since. After that one talk on, I have been invited to serve at other seminars and spiritual retreats, sometimes at people's homes and nonprofit organizations, always sharing about how faith, prayer, and service to others helped me to heal. Prayer is a connection with God. Prayer begins with the affirmation that there is a divine being with infinite love and wisdom with whom we can communicate, something that we cannot see or describe but know exists.

Faith refers to things that are not seen;
and hope, to things that are not within reach.
THOMAS AQUINAS

Many ways to pray exist: using words, in silence and contemplation, or by singing, praising, writing, or reciting creeds like the rosary or the yapa mala used in Hinduism and Buddhism. Believing that an unseen God is listening and is present within you requires silence. We may even hear God giving us advice and respond to our petitions, conversations, thankfulness, sorrows, and repentance if we are convinced that what we are asking for will be granted to us. If God exists, and we are connected to God, then what we need matters and every request will be granted. However, this connection must be established by us because God gave us free will and waits for us.

To find this connection is like tuning to a radio station: as you search for the station, you hear all this static noise until you finally get to the right spot where the transmission sounds nice and clear. To be able to tune to God's station, we must be in silence without the noise of daily life. Understand that every request will be granted is difficult because many times what we ask for does not come to fruition and most people, to avoid being disappointed, stop trying and begin accepting the idea of destiny. They are convinced that things are just the way they are, and no possibility to change the outcome exists.

You know of someone beating the odds surviving a terminal illness or someone who unexpectedly comes out of a comma or survive a horrible accident, or even someone getting the ideal job, and you may ask why such good fortune does not happen to you. Well, I have good news for you:

God will answer your prayers every single time at the proper moment, but you must pray with faith that you will receive what you are asking for.

When you pray, go into your room,
close the door and pray to your Father, who is unseen.
Then your Father, who sees what is done in secret,
will reward you.
MATTHEW 6:6

I personally know many people whose faith and prayer played an integral part to overcome grave problems and situations. For those who have beaten the odds and have been blessed with the joy of continuing to live, found the job of their dreams, met their ideal partner, or realized their dreams, do they believe it was luck? Was it destiny? Does God answer prayers to some but not to others? I am not prepared to answer these questions for you. However, I know from my own experience that those who faithfully ask and are open to receive, eventually receive what they asked for.

Until now you have not asked
for anything in my name.
Ask and you will receive,
and your joy will be complete.
JOHN 16:24

As Chambao, the singer and song writer describe in one of her songs: "Those who ask, shall receive if they know what they are asking and how to make the call."

I find the fact interesting that we tend to pray when we are in distress or in desperate need for something, but when everything is going well in our lives and we are happy and joyful, we normally do not think of praying in thankfulness for everything we have, particularly for health and life. We just take our blessings for granted. We move God to the side, but God does not care. God is always willing to help. Exceptional people throughout the ages, believers of different backgrounds, philosophies, and religions, have used prayer to connect to God, and in their own ways, they explain that their capacity to engage with God is rooted in all of us. God shows up when we surrender. God's infinite love and mercy are there in the silence of our hearts. I testify to this truth because it works for me every time I acknowledge I cannot do it alone and humbly ask for forgiveness and surrender. The rest of my days I give thanks for the blessings I receive, especially for my health.

After my second surgery, which was a lymphadenectomy in which twenty-three lymph nodes were removed from the lower part of my right ear through my neck and up to my right shoulder and included removing a muscle and a nerve and in which three of the lymph nodes were positive and also included a four-month treatment with interferon alfa 2b, the cancer returned under my left ear. Those four months were very hard. I had strong flu symptoms day after day and dropped close to twenty pounds. The cancer came back with a strong likelihood that it could spread to other distant areas of my body. I was hoping this rough physical and mental experience caused by the treatment was doing the same thing to the cancer cells, but the interferon treatment did not work. I remember driving to my surgeon oncologist's office to receive the results of a biopsy he had performed on a lymph node under my left ear. Naomi left work early to meet me there.

He said, "Mr. Cordoba, the results came back positive." "This means the treatment did not work?" I asked. "I am afraid not," he answered. I remember my wife's face as she looked down to the floor. I wondered what she was thinking and feeling. Perhaps she feared losing me; perhaps she was wondering how she would manage to raise five young children alone. "Now what Doctor? What are we going to do now?" I asked. The doctor said: "I ordered a PET scan for Monday to make sure there are no other spots in your body. The earliest I could get you in is Monday." It was Wednesday. This suggested the gravity of the situation. I thought the doctor did not want to waste any time. Although, he assured me that biologically, the melanoma cells, though very aggressive, did not grow that fast. Monday was fine.

My wife interrupted and asked the doctor what were the possibilities that there were more tumors in other parts of the body. He said he did not like to answer those types of questions because everyone was different. Ultimately, the chances of me having other tumors spread throughout the body were high. At that moment I realized that my situation was not in the hands of doctors. However, I felt a warm and peaceful sensation throughout my body; I felt calm and strong. I accepted the news and thanked the doctor, looked at him in the eyes, shook his hand, and held my wife's hand as we walked out of the room and headed toward the elevators.

While we were waiting for our cars, Naomi held my hand and looked at me; her eyes showed anxiety, stress, and fear. "What are we going to do now?" she asked me. I am sure that what she wanted to say was that the treatment did not work and the doctors had no clear answers for us. I can still see and feel that moment as if it were today. I do not have words to describe the calmness and strength I had in that moment. I remember looking deeply into her eyes and telling her that I could not explain what I was feeling, but I knew that in one way or another everything was going to be all right, because somehow I felt we were in God's hands and God would be with us through our process. This came straight from the heart. I gave her a hug and asked her to follow me to church and meet me in the prayer chapel.

I got there before Naomi and entered the chapel, which at the time was empty. I walked to the altar, fell on my knees, and burst into tears, letting it all out: from the first diagnosis, the biopsies, the surgery on my scalp, the second intervention where they removed the lymph nodes and used the Interferon treatment. All the feelings, fear, countless questions about what would happen to my family, anxiety, stress, all the time I lost doing unimportant things, my faults, and the things I failed to do because I did not have time, everything came out at the altar. I prayed. I said to God: "Heavenly Father, today I understood that this situation is truly in your hands. I asked for great doctors and nurses, and you gave me the best ones. They are doing the best they can but, in the end, everything is in your hands. I surrender to you; please take control. I am sorry for all my faults no matter how insignificant they were; forgive me for the things I have failed to do. If it is possible, I ask you for a little more time to be a better husband, the best father, and the best friend I can be and to be able to serve others in need."

As I was praying, I began to feel the peace and calmness that I had felt before we left the doctor's office. Suddenly, still kneeling facing the altar with my eyes closed, I heard the door open. I figured it was Naomi. I felt a hand pressing my right shoulder and a female voice telling me: "Young man please pray for me because I just found out that I have cancer." I held her hand, opened my eyes, and turned to look at her. "For sure mam," I said, "may I ask your name?" She looked to be in her seventies. "My name is Teresa," she said. "Okay, I will start right now." She thanked me and blessed me. I turned back to the altar and began to pray for Teresa's health. I heard the door opening and again I figured it was Naomi. When I stopped praying for Teresa, I stood up to sit and noticed she was gone. I sat and embraced the experience, trying to understand what had just happened, and realized that God was listening to my petitions and brought Teresa to the chapel as a signal for me to experience the power of surrender and prayer. Amen for that. Naomi finally entered the chapel, and we stayed in silence with a sense of peace and trust. From that unforgettable experience at the chapel, prayer began to be essential throughout my battle and for the rest of my life.

I had an appointment with my oncologist the next day. It was a very intense week. From the biopsy to test results, the phone rang all week, day and night. By Friday afternoon, all I wanted to do was to be in silence without any more distractions. Naomi took the boys to soccer practice and would not return until 6:30 p.m. Finally, everything got very quiet. As I closed my eyes and tried to relax, the phone rang. My first thought was to let it ring and let the caller to leave a voice message, but I then I thought: whoever was calling was thinking of us and deserved an answer. I answered the phone. The caller was one of my childhood friends, who lives close to us.

He called to invite me to join him and his wife in a prayer group. I was very thankful for the invitation, but I told him that I would join them the following Friday because I was exhausted from a week full of ups and downs and the upcoming PET scan I was going for on Monday. He insisted and said that precisely because of how I was feeling I should go. I felt his love and intention to help me. How could I block that blessing?

I accepted. I was grateful for the invitation. I told him I would go not only for me but to pray for his autistic son. I remember during my experience at the chapel asking God to give me a little time to help others. As I was praying, Teresa showed up in the chapel and asked me to pray for her, and now I had an opportunity to pray with a group of people for my friend's son. I forgot about myself and focused on going to join this prayer group to pray for my friends' situation. My friend insisted on picking us up at 7:30 p.m.

The Catholic Charismatic Prayer Group started praying the divine mercy, followed by singing and praising God. I joined enthusiastically, focusing on my friends' autistic son. I closed my eyes and began to feel joy and a sense of calm and thankfulness for being there with these faithful brothers and sister. I was embracing the spiritual experience and suddenly one of the nuns from the St. Catherine of Siena charismatic movement took by the hand and led me to the altar. The sister held my hand until we reached the altar where the priest was placing his hands and praying for each person who got in front of him. As I walked toward the altar, I began to experience the same warm feeling I had felt at the doctor's office. I listened to the father and one of the nuns utter words I could not understand, and when my turn came, I remember feeling a very hot stream of light blue water flowing from the top of my head through my throat. I also remember seeing a small white figure and hearing a voice telling me that everything would be fine. I fell to the ground.

The results of the PET scan exam that I had on Monday came out negative, which meant no other spots of cancer existed in my body. I was scheduled for my third surgery, a lymphadenectomy from the back of my left ear down through my neck and left shoulder. This time, they removed twenty-two lymph nodes two of which came our positive, but this time there was no need to remove any muscles or nerves. As per treatment options, in this occasion they applied GM-CSF, an experimental noninvasive peptide believed to booster my immune system. I injected myself fifteen subcutaneous shots per month then suspended the treatment for fifteen days then started the cycle again for twelve months.

From my experience at the chapel, I began to understand the importance of opening my heart to receive with gratitude and humility everything that was lovingly and sincerely offered to me. I began to see my situation as a battle, and I was certain I was going to come out of it victorious. In total, I went through ten surgeries (three of them craniotomies), two Gamma Knife procedures, chemotherapy and radiotherapy treatments, and interferon and GM-CSF. Prayer and acceptance became part of my life. I knew that, somehow, I would be victorious in this fight. But what happened to all those recurrences? Why did God not stop them? Good questions, but the way I explain them is that I came out of each of the surgeries, especially those of the brain, without complications that could have damaged my motor skills or my vision and even caused my death. I was always grateful for the fact that surgery was an option, although one time two of the tumors could not be removed.

I continued praying and meditating. I continued to see my body at the cellular level, imagining a creature, like Pac-Man, eating the cancer cells that floated around. I continued to see and feel the love of God through a clear blue healing ray that penetrated my body from the top of my head flowing to my feet. I prayed and meditated at least twice a day. I received the news on Monday that the doctor had scheduled the craniotomy (my sixth surgery and third craniotomy) for Thursday. I was told that, in this occasion, they would begin the surgery with local anesthesia because the tumor was located very close to the motor area of speech. First, they had to try making me talk, and if they concluded that it was not dangerous to continue, then they would apply general anesthesia.

I was scheduled to undergo a magnetic resonance as a preoperative procedure, which would be performed with a helmet that would indicate to the surgeon the exact tumor position. This would happen on Wednesday, the day before surgery, and on Thursday I should arrive early at the hospital. On Monday night, hours after the meeting with my neurosurgeon, I received a call from Daniela, another childhood friend who knew I was fighting cancer but had no idea of my situation at that time. She explained that the previous week she had dreamed of me and had awakened with the urgency of inviting me to her prayer group at the

Saint Luis Church. She apologized for calling just the night before but explained that she was not sure what I would think about her dream, the invitation to the prayer group, and a meeting with Maria de los Angeles, a woman with the gift to heal by the laying of hands. Again, as in the case of the invitations from my other friends, I felt Dani's intention to give me love, and I was open to receive the love she had for me. I immediately told her the news that I had received just hours before about my next surgery. She was very happy that I accepted her invitation and that I would be there.

As soon as we finished our conversation and hung up the phone, I told my wife about Daniela's dream and invitation. I ended up going alone because my wife had to pick up the children at soccer practice. I arrived before 8:00 p.m. and was received by my friend Daniela, who was very happy to see me. She invited me to sit where I wanted. I went directly to the front bench, near the altar, which had a picture of the Jesus of Mercy. I knelt and began to pray, thanking God for my friend's invitation; I was eager to meet Maria de los Angeles. Upon arrival I was told that she had just returned with a strong cold from a missionary trip through Guatemala and did not feel good to impose her hands, but she would be in the attached chapel praying for all of us.

When we finished the prayer of the divine mercy and began to sing and praise, I occasionally asked for a successful surgery. María de los Angeles came out of the room and asked my friend where I was because she wanted to meet me. Daniela told me that she walked toward me with a determined step. I felt an older woman's hand take my arm, but this time she called me by my name. She introduced herself and asked me to follow her to the back of the church because she wanted to pray for me. I must remind you that my brain surgery would take place in only two days. When we got to the back, she asked me to sit in front of her. She placed her hands on my head and began to pray. I began to feel a current of water flow through my body, and tears began to flow uncontrollably. Once again, I heard words that I could not understand, but I knew they were definitely healing me. As soon as she stopped praying, she blessed me and told me that, while praying, she felt that I was about to go through something important during the week. I smiled and told her that I was going to undergo brain surgery on Thursday to remove a malignant tumor of melanoma. She asked me where the tumor was located. I showed her all three: the one they were going to extract and the other two, which were inoperable. She placed both hands on those areas and asked God to heal my illness completely. I returned to my bench, drying my healing tears. At the end of the wonderful prayer session, Maria de los Angeles asked everyone to elevate a prayer for me because on Thursday I would undergo an intervention to remove a brain tumor. Then she told everyone that she would not be surprised if I did not have to undergo the surgery because, "I do not ask God in little, I demand that he use his healing power." Daniela was speechless about what happened with María de los Angeles and the fact of having seen her leave the room with a strong desire to know me and to pray by laying hands on me.

When I got home, I shared everything that had happened with Naomi. She, in turn, told me that she had noticed something on my face when she saw me come in and that she immediately knew something had happened. I told her that I would pray about it and that I would sleep trusting God would have an answer for me regarding the possibility of going ahead with surgery or canceling it. I woke up and told Naomi that I would go ahead and undergo surgery. I went to the hospital to have an MRI and went back early Thursday morning. The surgery was scheduled for 9:00 a.m. They assigned me a room and told us that the doctor would come to talk to us right before they took me to the operating room.

Shortly afterwards the doctor arrived with a radiant smile. He seemed to be very happy. He greeted us and told us he had two pieces of good news and asked me which one I would like to hear first. Naomi and I looked at each other and smiled. He told us that the first one was that he had conferenced with colleagues from other hospitals in the country and had concluded that there was no need to operate on me awake because the tumor was far enough from the speech area. The second piece of news was that the two inoperable tumors had not appeared on the previous day's MRI. Once again, Naomi and I looked at each other in total understanding and gratitude to God. The doctor told us that they would verify the MRI findings when performing the postoperative magnetic resonance.

As in my two previous craniotomies, they presented me with a list of possible risks and results and asked me a question that I would have to answer when I woke from the surgery. As always, just before I fell asleep, I prayed for my beautiful family, my neurosurgeon, and his surgical team, thanking God for my life. Before applying anesthesia, my surgeon asked me a question: "How do you say yellow in Spanish?" I woke up from the surgery and once again my answer, "amarillo," was correct. The surgery had been successful. The postoperative magnetic resonance indicated that the tumor had been successfully removed and confirmed that the two inoperable tumors had disappeared.

Prayer is an intimate and open conversation with God, and this means that we speak and listen. During this conversation, the infinite love of God is liberated, and things begin to happen. Whether the prayer is for welfare, healing, love, an act of gratitude, or to intercede for someone, we begin to receive more than we ask for and more than we can be thankful for.

Apart from life itself, prayer can be the best and most powerful gift that has been given to us, a conversation with the creator of all things, a gift that very few find because it is inside of us and requires a little time that we usually say we do not have. Through my faith, I asked for and received this amazing gift, which helped a great deal in reversing my cancer and returning my health, but I must say that helping others without expectations also accelerated my healing and deepened my relationship with God.

We can change the course of events
if we kneel and pray with faith.
BILLY GRAHAM.

Learning to Receive

When a person gives from the heart and another receives with an open heart, a divine channel opens where God, the infinite source of love and wisdom, creates miracles. Faith, prayer, service, giving, and receiving are ingredients that all go into the same blender and produce a smoothie of peace, tranquility, physical, emotional, mental, and spiritual health. This drink contains the necessary nutrients to be able to connect with God, but as we stop taking it, we momentarily lose our synchronicity with God. Giving, helping others, being supportive and compassionate, serving others without expectations are very valuable virtues, but it is equally important and part of the balance in life to receive.

Jesus, through love and his own actions, teaches us the importance of serving others, and in the same way he offers us through his miracles many examples in which people open their hearts and receive with faith God's healing love. In each miracle, we see the disposition of the needy to receive the love of God through Jesus. We see the teacher devoutly giving, and, on the other hand, the individual open to receive. Curiously, many people never find the balance between giving and receiving. It is much easier to give than to receive. Why is it harder for us to receive? Why is it hard to be loved? Do we not understand that allowing ourselves to receive what others offer is the only way we can open the channel of love that produces miracles? Receiving is easy to talk about it, but why do most people find it so hard? Their attitude and willingness to give is very different from the attitude they assume when they are offered something. Why do we have trouble accepting?

Maybe people are afraid that whoever gives will demand something in return. By digging a little, we realize that some people have low self-esteem and do not consider themselves worthy of love and attention. This may be because at some point they have been hurt, or they have hurt others and are convinced that they do not deserve to receive anything from others, especially love. Self-rejection prevents them from feeling comfortable when receiving and letting themselves be loved.

Depending on the culture in which an individual was raised, that person may have formed the image of a cruel and sententious God who will condemn people for misbehaving. I remember my parents and relatives telling me that God would punish me if I behaved badly. Basically, we grew up in trauma caused by erroneous tactics, driven by our different cultures, including the fear-based methods employed by our teachers, priests, or rabbis in religious schools. We then grow and live unconsciously with these patterns. God is love and mercy. God is not a judge who expects us to fail to then sentence us; on the contrary, God rather waits with open arms for children to return home humbly. God's love is infinite and eternal. Unfortunately, I had to go through the experience of a cancer and, with such a delicate diagnosis, to then begin to let myself be loved and appreciate with gratitude the gifts that were offered to me during my situation. My wife and children were part of this as well. Receiving begins to occur when you lower your guard and become humble, surrendering before God and surrendering your situation. Ironically, these things become easier when you survive a fatal accident or a heart attack, or when you are sick with cancer or another chronic disease.

My healing began the moment I began to open myself with gratitude to the love that all people gave my family and me through their gifts, whether they cooked food for dinner time so that Naomi had less work to do; took the children to school or to their sports, dance, or art activities; gave us moral and spiritual help or prayers; or simply were on the look out to do for us whatever we needed. On all these occasions, I felt the hand of God through angels who were present during my battle. It is not necessary that you go through extreme experiences in your life to learn to receive. You should simply look for what prevents you from letting yourself be loved, that is, the reasons why you may not ask

God more often or the causes why you do not love yourself. Why the self-rejection?

Freeing yourself from self-rejection and devoting love and compassion to yourself is the initial step in the development of the gift of receiving, but for this a person needs faith or to banish fear and open to sharing. First you must love yourself. You cannot give or serve unless you first give to yourself. The same is true for receiving: unless you are capable of receiving love, it is not possible for you to understand what it is to receive. Find the reasons that do not allow you to receive love.

There is no lack of resources.
There is no competition for resources.
We are only accepting or rejecting what we are asking for.
ESTHER HICKS,Teachings of Abraham

It is not easy to understand this truth because we convince ourselves that for some reason what we asked for was not granted, or we noticed the same in other people close to us. We are the ones who block the reception of what we have asked for and has already been granted.

The petition has already been made,
the answer is also in place,
but permission to enter has not occurred.
ESTHER HICKS

In the third chapter of the book of Revelation says: "Look, I knock at the door; If you listen and open, then I will come in and have dinner together" (Revelation 3:20). In this scripture, we see that God is not imposing, does not force the door to enter our hearts. He knocks and gives us the freedom to decide whether we open or not. God suggests that we open the door and receive what we ask for. God asks for permission to enter and eat with us. Amen for the unconditional love of God. Dear friends, clearly, we are the ones who reject what we ask for; we are the ones who close up when people want to give to us. This divine formula of peace and communion that allows miracles of all kinds to occur can only occur when the one offering does it from love, without any agenda, and the one who receives accepts from love and with gratitude the offering. It is a fusion of love in giving and love in receiving. One does not work without the other.

As for what you ask in your prayers, opening the door to receive what you have asked for is key. God has already given to you what you have asked for and is truly the best for you. In cases where someone asks you, give without prejudice according to your abilities, and in cases where you have not been asked, but you see people in need, help them according to your possibilities. God is present in all these cases. Everyone who serves others by giving of their time, their talents, and their treasures is really God working. You are the hands of God in action, and the one who receives feels God through your actions.

Let us stop blocking the miracles that can occur daily, whenever there is a need, and someone is willing to give. "Because I was hungry, and you gave me food; I was thirsty, and you gave me to drink; I was a stranger, and you picked me up; I was naked, and you dressed me" (Matthew 25:35). This divine formula of giving and receiving applies to you. During your journey, your roles change; sometimes you are the giver and sometimes you are needy, but God is always present.

Nutrition

A ccording to the Webster Dictionary "nutrition is the act or process of nourishing or being nourished; specifically the sum of the processes by which and animal or plant takes in and utilizes food substances." People undergoing treatment must understand what nutrition is and tune into their bodies to help them recover their original healthy design. People should make sure to use their energy to fight or prevent disease, instead of consuming it to clean up the toxins they consume when they eat, which is especially important if they are sick.

Whether it's compromised immune systems,
cells devastated by treatment medications
or the extreme stress of the disease itself,
It is essential that those patients with cancer

make each quantity of calories
optimize their chances of recovery.
TY BOLLINGER

I mentioned earlier about my visit to the naturopathic doctor of "alternative medicine" and how, after this meeting, I came away convinced that I had to radically change what I was allowing to be done regarding my chemotherapy and radiotherapy treatments. At the end of the day, you could say that these chemicals were part of my diet because I was allowing them to enter my body. The doctor clearly explained to me the problem with chemical treatments through an example that made a lot of sense to me: "What would happen if you did not keep the kitchen clean?" Finally, ants and cockroaches would appear again, right? You would probably call a fumigation company; they would go to your house and spray their chemical products to kill them. This type of approach works temporarily because if you keep your old patterns and leave your kitchen dirty again, the insects will sooner or later return."

Undoubtedly, it is a surprising metaphor for conventional chemotherapy and radiation treatments. According to this methodology, many people go into remission, but if they do not change their eating habits and their patterns of life, the disease will eventually return. The doctor also told me in detail how to keep my body's pH levels balanced because cancer cells are engulfed in acidic systems. He went on to explain the serious reality that our society consumes acidic foods, such as red meat, alcohol, and processed sugar, a friendly environment for cancer cells to grow. In fact, he explained that the common denominator of most diseases is a body with an acidic pH. Most of us never consider the acid-alkaline balance of our blood, but an adequate pH is a crucial aspect for health. Many doctors emphasize its importance because a balanced pH protects us from the inside out. Disease and disorder, they say, cannot take root in a body whose pH is in equilibrium.

Why is pH crucial for health? As I have already mentioned, the imbalance between acidity and alkalinity allows unhealthy organisms to flourish, damages tissues and organs, and compromises the immune system. You may be asking yourself: what is the pH? What is the appropriate pH? Very simple: pH is a nomenclature for the hydrogen potential, which is a measure of the acidity or alkalinity of a substance, in this case of the fluids and tissues of our body. Bodily pH is measured with a strip of paper specially designed for that purpose. The result is presented on a scale of 0 to 14. The more acidic a solution is, the lower its value; the more alkaline, the higher the number. The optimal measurement is a pH of 7.3 and the normal range is between 6 and 7.5.

High levels of acidity force our bodies to steal minerals from bones, cells, organs, and tissues. The cells end up lacking enough minerals to properly dispose of the waste and oxygenate completely. The absorption of vitamins is compromised by the loss of minerals. Toxins and pathogens accumulate in the body, and the immune system is suppressed. Now, I offer you a partial list of causes of acidity in your body: alcohol and drugs, antibiotics, sugar substitutes, chronic stress, low levels of fiber, lack or excess of exercise, excess meat, hormones in food, some health and beauty products, plastics, colors and preservatives used in food, pesticides, pollution, processed and refined foods, and superficial respiration.

On the other hand, we must be careful not to have an alkaline imbalance: the excess of alkalinity in the body can cause gastrointestinal problems and skin irritations. Too much alkalinity can also shake the normal pH of the body, which leads to metabolic alkalosis, a condition that can produce the following symptoms: nausea, vomiting, and kidney damage due to mineral imbalance. The doctor gave me a brochure with information about the foods and drinks that produce acid in the body, as well as the foods and beverages that help to alkalize it to maintain a balanced pH. Something that he recommends from the beginning is to stay away from sodas because they have extremely high amounts of sugar and chemicals that produce acid in our bodies. A can of soda contains nine teaspoons of sugar, and it would take thirty-two glasses of water to eliminate the acid produced by that single drink. By the way, the chemicals used to replace the sugar contained in a can of dietary soda produce more acid than a can of regular soda. This is very important advice, not only for patients with cancer, but also to prevent diseases.

What you eat may
be the most powerful medicine
or the slowest way to poison you.
ANN WIGMORE

Links to websites with helpful information, some of which I have touched on, are at the end of the book. Everything I heard and read made sense to me, so I signed up for the naturopath's treatment, which consisted of two phases and included two noninvasive scans to compare my system before and after detoxification. I undertook the first phase, which lasted twenty-one days and was designed to eliminate all the foods that produce acid in the body from my diet. During that time, I had to take probiotic products to clean myself: juices, vegetables, and some fruits. The results were amazing. In just a week, I began to feel the difference: my energy levels increased, my eyes began to shine, and my general behavior improved. Friends and family noticed something different in my physical appearance.

The second scan and the comparison with the first was simply incredible, a highly motivating factor to continue with this new way of fighting my disease from that moment. As Dr. Axe points out: "Food is medicine." How could that be? I had not felt that way since I was diagnosed. The answer is very simple: I had begun to help my body to fight the disease, on the one hand, by stopping intoxicating it with unhealthy food and drinks, and on the other, by consuming the necessary nutrients to balance my pH levels, strengthen my immune system, and help my body, at the cellular level, back to its natural state.

I decided not to take the capsules of chemotherapy for the brain during the detoxification period, and the results were so obvious that in the next visit I had with my oncologist, I told him that I would not receive more chemotherapy treatments. The doctor asked me several times if I was sure of my decision, and every time I answered yes. I told him that it had been a long time since I had felt so well. Of course, I continued to go on with my follow-up exams, and since I already had tumors in my brain and some were operable, I obviously opted to have those that could be operated on extracted.

Dear friend, my intention is to share what I learned and applied with faith through my battle, as well as everything that helped me to heal to give you encouragement and hope by reading the book. By no means do I suggest that you make the same decisions, particularly those that have to do with suspending conventional treatments. My strategy of abandoning these therapies and continuing with the follow-up and the necessary surgeries was successful, and I feel my duty is to share it, but each person must make their own decisions. For me it was and still is a strategy in which, everywhere, God has been present. In faith, prayer, meditation, service, forgiveness, love, positive attitude, and nutrition, God is present, but in the same way God is present in science and our advances in medicine. Without the talent and dedication of my doctors, I would not be here today. In everything, absolutely everything, God is present.

The doctor of the future
will not treat the human body with drugs,
but will rather cure and prevent
diseases with NUTRITION.
THOMAS EDISON

Epilogue

Being diagnosed with cancer, no matter what type or how advanced it may be, is something I do not wish for anyone. As you have probably noticed, my message is also to those who have not been affected by the disease, to prevent cancer and other diseases that could appear due to the same causes: stress, interpersonal conflicts, inability to forgive, carelessness, inappropriate eating habits, lack of exercise, and lack of rest through prayer and meditation. Now, if you have been diagnosed with cancer, allow me to reiterate the importance of fighting with some or all the tools discussed in this book that make sense to you.

Remember:

- You own your situation.

- You are the person most interested in your health.

- Your body was designed to be healthy.

- A root cause for your diagnosis exists.

- The diagnosis probably has nothing to do with your family history.

- Your doctors are part of your team, but you are the captain.

- Learn to receive what your friends and family want to give you.

- Forgive, pray, and meditate.

- Do not pay attention to statistics because you are your own statistic.

- Look for survivors to share experiences and motivate you.

- Leave your disease or situation at home and go out to do the things you like to do.

- Help others even if you are not feeling well.

- You reap what you sow.

- Ask and you shall receive.

Have faith that each of these tips will heal you and reverse your current affliction, returning you to the natural and healthy state in which you were born. Looking back, I can say that this process has been a blessing for me. Today I appreciate my health and my life. I appreciate nature much more, and I feel connected with nature. I hug trees, and I am filled with their healing energy; I give thanks for a new day when I wake up every morning and again when I go to bed; I give thanks for the things that I achieved and received from others; for my children, my friends, and the people who are under my professional leadership. When I can, I wait and watch the sunrise, the sunset, and the full moon. In short, I am grateful to be part of this beautiful planet. Do you know how much God loves you?

Nobody knows when they will die, but we all know that we will leave one day. In this sense, neither you nor I know if we will be here tomorrow, the day after tomorrow, next month, or next year. This tells me that we should fully appreciate today, love, share, give, receive, and appreciate each moment, whether sick or well. Today is the first day of the rest of your life. I remember reading a reflection of Mother Teresa of Calcutta where she explained what it meant for her to go to the cemetery and read the dates of birth and death of a human being and reflected on the line between those two dates. For her, the line meant the time you were here and what you did or did not do in that period.

I hope you don't mind
that I put down into words
how wonderful life is
while you are in the world
SIR ELTON JOHN

The disciples were full of questions
about God. Said the master;
"God is the unknown and the unknowable.
every statement about Him,
every answer to your questions,
is a distortion of the truth."
The disciples were bewildered.
"Then why do you speak about Him at all?"
"Why does the bird sing?" said the master.
Not because it has a statement,
but because it has a song.
The words of the scholar are to be understood.
The words of the master are not to be understood.
They are to be listened to as one listens to the wind
in the trees and the sound of the river
and the song of the bird,
they will awaken something within the heart
that is beyond knowledge
ANTHONY DE MELLO

Sources

CANCER

National Cancer Institute: https://www.cancer.gov/espanol/politicas/link

Melanoma: http://www.skincancer.org/skin-cancer-information/melanoma

Spanish Association against Cancer: https://www.aecc.es

Statistics: https://seer.cancer.gov

NUTRITION

BALANCE OF pH AND HEALTH:

https://draxe.com/balancing-act-why-ph-is-crucial-to-health/

Detoxify: https://thetruthaboutcancer.com/12-ways-to-prepare-detox- cleanse /

Page of Dr. Ax: https://draxe.com

Oxygen against cancer: http://www.cancerfightingstrategies.com/oxygen-and-cancer.html

Cure cancer naturally: https://curacancernatural.org

GUIDED MEDITATION

Relaxing Music & Affirmations for a Peaceful Life: https://youtu.be/tOQaVSX-N4c

Ho'oponopono ancient Hawaiian prayer: https://youtu.be/CUHf4dmslro

Surrender Meditation (letting go of control): https://youtu.be/KfEqviC7rwg

Quiet mind for anxiety and negative thoughts: https://youtu.be/krKXXmnLQ8o

Manifest you dreams: https://youtu.be/kC6so_Z5mGg

BOOKS

Albom, Mitch (1984). *For One More Day.* Hyperion, Nueva York.

Albom, Mitch (2003). *The Five People You Meet in Heaven.* Hyperion, Nueva York.

Albom, Mitch (2009). *Have a little faith.* Hyperion, Nueva York.

De Mello, Anthony (1982). *The song of the bird.* Doubleday, New York.

Girard, Vickie (2001). *There is no Place like Hope.* Compendium, Inc., Washington.

Murphy, Joseph (1982). *The Power of your Subconscious Mind.* Jeremy P. Tarcher/Pinguen, Nueva York.

Sharma, Robin (1999). *Who will Cry when you Die?* Hay House, Toronto.

Sharma, Robin (2013). *The Saint, The Surfer and the CEO.* Hay House, California.

Tolle, Eckart (2004). *The Power of Now.* New World Library & Namaste Publishing, California.

Health and wellness news: https://www.takingcharge.csh.umn.
edu/think-and-feel-health

On spirituality in healing: https://www.fmcpaware.org/the-role-
of-spirituality-in- healing.html

Reasons to stay positive: http://www.oprah.com/health/how-your-
emotions-affect- your-health-and-immune-system

Quotes

"This is the day which the Lord has made; let us rejoice and be glad in it." Psalm 118, 24

"If we could clearly see the miracle of a flower, our lives would change." Buddha

"It is love that has brought you here. It is love that accompanies you on this trip. It is love that gives you every chance to change everything." Anthony de Mello

"There are two ways of living. One is as though nothing is a miracle. The other is as if everything is a miracle" Albert Einstein

"Because I know very well the plans I have for you," says the Lord; plans of well-being and not of calamity, in order to give them a future and and hope." Jeremiah 29, 11

"You are not here accidentally, but in a very significant way. If you do not cling to any concept, object or ideology, it will be easy for you to discover what is the truth and the reality." Anthony de Mello

"I hope you do not mind that I put into words how wonderful life is while you are in the world." Elton John

"Look for those wonderful things that most people do not do. Give gifts of love to those whom others ignore." Paramahansa Yogananda

"In truth I tell you, if anyone says to this mountain, 'Be pulled up and thrown into the sea,' with no doubt in his heart, but believing that what he says will happen, it will be." Mark 11:23

"Prayer is not an old woman's amusement. Properly understood and applied, it is the most potent instrument of action." Mahatma Gandhi

"The simple way: silence is prayer, prayer is faith, faith is love, love is service, the fruit of service is peace." Mother Teresa

"Life is like riding a bicycle. To keep your balance, you must keep moving." Albert Einstein

"Living is the strangest thing in the world. The majority of people exist, that's all." Oscar Wilde

"Behind the clouds the sun always shines." Anonymous

About the Author

F more than seventeen years, Georges Córdoba has dedicated much of his time to serving the needy through social projects such as: programs for children with aids, support for shelters administered by the Florida Department of Social Services, organization of groups for the purchase and distribution of water and food for people living on the streets, and leadership of ministries dedicated to bringing people closer to God.

© Francisco González

Georges is a survivor of an advanced cancer that, as he himself expresses it: "radically changed the purpose of my existence; cancer is the reason why the real life I was born to live began". As a result of his experience, he joined social programs such as The Road to Recovery, of the American Cancer Society where as a volunteer recruited and coordinated his fellow volunteers in Miami Dade Florida, and at the same time began to give talks in hospitals, churches and spiritual and health retreats.

After having worked as a software engineer and executive, Georges is now a Health and Life Purpose Coach, a Reiki Master and an Author. He is dedicated to changing lives through transformational coaching, self-growth workshops, and Reiki workshops. His goal is to encourage as many people as possible to "Live in wellness, learn and share, and most importantly, reconnect with themselves." He is a founding member of QualeVita, LLC, (Quality of life).

Good Morning, Sunrise is Georges' debut book.

www.qualevita.com
coach.georges
@healthcoachgeorges
coach.georges@qualevita.com

Index

Good Morning, Sunrise
it was printed in USA with
editorial production of
La Agencia de la Palabra
in March 2019